Everyday Number Sense

Mental Math and Visual Models

STUDENT BOOK

TERC

Mary Jane Schmitt, Myriam Steinback,
Tricia Donovan, and Martha Merson

Key Curriculum Press
Innovators in Mathematics Education

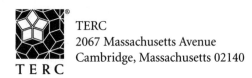

TERC
2067 Massachusetts Avenue
Cambridge, Massachusetts 02140

Key College Publishing and Key Curriculum Press
Development Editor: Erika Shaffer
Production Director: McKinley Williams
Production Project Manager: Ken Wischmeyer
Project Manager: Susan Yates
Consultant: Donna Curry
Text Designer: Laura Murray Productions
Proofreader: Publication Services
Photo Researcher: Laura Murray Productions
Art and Design Coordinator: Jensen Barnes
Cover and Logo Design: Kavitha Becker, Marilyn Perry
Cover Photo Credit: Jensen Barnes
Printer: Alonzo Printing

Editorial Director: Richard J. Bonacci
Vice President/General Manager: Mike Simpson
Publisher: Steven Rasmussen

EMPower Research and Development Team
Principal Investigator: Myriam Steinback
Co-Principal Investigator: Mary Jane Schmitt
Research Associate: Martha Merson
Curriculum Developers: Donna Curry, Tricia Donovan

Technical Team
Production and Design Coordinator: Valerie Martin
Project Assistant and Graphic Designer: Juania Ashley
Copyeditor: Jill Pellarin

Evaluation Team
Brett Consulting Group:
    Belle Brett
    Marilyn Matzko

EMPower™ was developed at TERC in Cambridge, Massachusetts. This material is based upon work supported by the National Science Foundation under award number ESI-9911410 and by the Education Research Collaborative at TERC. Any opinions, findings, and conclusions or recommendations expressed in this publication are those of the authors and do not necessarily reflect the views of the National Science Foundation.

TERC is a not-for-profit education research and development organization dedicated to improving mathematics, science, and technology teaching and learning.

Key Curriculum Press
1150 65th Street
Emeryville, CA 94608
510-595-7000
editorial@keycollege.com
www.keypress.com

Printed in the United States of America
10 9 8 7 6 5 4 3 2 1   08 07 06 05

ISBN 1-55953-726-4

Contents

Introduction

Welcome to EMPower

Students using the EMPower books often find that EMPower's approach to mathematics is different from the approach found in other math books. For some students, it is new to talk about mathematics and to work on math in pairs or groups. The math in the EMPower books will help you connect the math you use in everyday life to the math you learn in your course.

We asked some students what they thought about EMPower's approach. We thought we would share some of their thoughts with you to help you know what to expect.

"It's more hands-on."

"More interesting."

"I use it in my life."

"We learn to work as a team."

"Our answers come from each other… [then] we work it out ourselves."

"Real-life examples like shopping and money are good."

"The lessons are interesting."

"I can help my children with their homework."

"It makes my brain work."

"Math is fun."

EMPower's goal is to make you think and to give you puzzles you will want to solve. Work hard. Work smart. Think deeply. Ask why.

Using This Book

This book is organized by lessons. Each lesson has the same format.

- The first page explains the lesson and states the purpose of the activity. Look for a question to keep in mind as you work.

- The activity page comes next. You will work on the activities in class, sometimes with a partner or in a group.

- Look for shaded boxes with additional information and ideas to help you get started if you become stuck.

- Practice pages follow the activities. These practices will make sense to you after you have done the activity. The four types of practice pages are

    Practice: provides another chance to see the math from the activity and to use new skills.

    Mental Math Practice: provides a chance to improve your speed with number skills.

    Extension: presents a challenge with a more difficult problem or a new but related math idea.

    Test Practice: asks a number of multiple-choice questions and one open-ended question.

In the *Appendices* at the end of the book, there is space for you to keep track of what you have learned and to record your thoughts about how you can use the information.

- Use notes, definitions, and drawings to help you remember new words in *Vocabulary*, pages 183–84.

- Answer the *Reflections* questions after each lesson, pages 185–92.

Tips for Success

Where do I begin?

Many people do not know where to begin when they look at their math assignments. If this happens to you, first try to organize your information.

Ask yourself:

What are some ways to "see" the problem?

Can I use objects, a diagram, or number line?

Much of this unit involves learning to do math in your head. We call this practice "mental math" because it allows you to work with numbers even when you don't have a pencil and paper or a calculator handy.

Ask yourself:

What patterns do I see in the numbers?

Can I build on facts I know?

I cannot do it. It seems too hard.

Make the numbers smaller. Deal with just a little bit of information at a time. Cross out the information you do not need.

Ask yourself:

Is there information in this problem I do not need?

Have I ever seen something like this before? What did I do then?

You can always look back at another lesson for ideas.

Am I done?

Don't walk away yet. Check your answers to make sure they make sense.

Ask yourself:

Did I include all the information I needed?

Is there another way to do the problem?

Check your math with a calculator. Ask others whether your work makes sense to them.

How does this connect to my life?

Every day you see numbers around you. In this book you look at numbers in new ways. You learn how to picture numbers and operations (x, ÷, +, −) in ways that will help you think faster on your feet, whether at work, in your community, or in classes. Along the way you will build your problem-solving skills while you learn about number lines, arrays, rounding, and estimating.

As you move in and out of class, think of all the ways you can total, compare, and divide amounts, and solve problems. Enjoy yourself as your understanding of numbers and operations grows!

Opening the Unit: Everyday Numbers

Where is math in your everyday life?

Before you start a new math topic, it is good to have an idea where you stand. Do you already know some of the material? Does it look hard? This lesson will help you and your teacher know what may be new or a review for you and what will challenge you in the weeks ahead.

This opening session is an assessment. There will be three tasks involving numbers and operations. Each one will help you figure out what you know and what you have yet to learn.

Activity 1: Where Is the Math in Your Life?

Fill out the chart below listing at least five ways you have used math or numbers in any way in the last month or so—money, time, measurement, or anything else requiring math.

How did you figure out your answer? Did you do the math in your head, with paper and pencil, or with a calculator? Did you do it another way?

Did you need an exact answer or an **estimate**?

Where and When I Used Math	In My Head (H) Calculator (C) Paper and Pencil (P)	Exact or Estimate?

Activity 2: Number of the Day

The number for today:

On the lines below, write as many expressions as you can whose answers equal the number for today. Use as many math operations and symbols as you can.

_____

_____

_____

_____

_____

_____

_____

_____

_____

_____

_____

_____

_____

Activity 3: Initial Assessment

First, you will do a **mental math** challenge. Then your teacher will show you some tasks and ask you to check off how you feel about your ability to solve each problem. In each case, check off one of the following:

____ Can do   ____ Don't know how   ____ Not sure

Everyday Number Sense:
Mental Math and Visual Models Unit Goals

What are your goals regarding everyday numbers? Review the following goals. Then think about your own goals and record them in the space provided.

- Solve problems mentally with estimates and exact answers.

- Represent operations ($x, \div, +, -$) using objects, pictures, arrays, and number lines to explain and support reasoning.

- Select appropriate operation(s) to represent problem situations (e.g., when to multiply and when to divide) and write expressions in mathematical notation.

- Explain and develop strategies for rounding, adjusting, and using benchmark numbers (10's and 100's) to solve problems.

- Use the scientific calculator.

My Own Goals

Close Enough with Mental Math

> **When do you do math in your head?**

People who are good with numbers do a lot of mental math. A person who is good at mental math depends on **rounding**. Rounding is often used to get an **approximate** answer, one that is "in the right ballpark," or close enough.

People routinely plan and budget in their everyday lives. "We want to have a playground in our community for our kids . . . about how much do we need to raise to purchase the equipment?" "I want to go to the Carribbean . . . about how much will I need to save out of my paycheck each week to be able to go next year?"

In this lesson, you will make a wish list of items to buy on a shopping spree. Using mental math, you will figure out how much money different combinations of items on your list would cost. You have to stay within a budget, so rounding will also help you keep track of how much money you have left to spend.

Activity 1: About How Much?

Your teacher will show you some amounts of money to add in your head. Using mental math, estimate the approximate **sum**.

Circle the closest answer for each problem.

1. a. $4   **b.** $5   **c.** $6

2. a. $15   **b.** $16   **c.** $17

3. a. $30   **b.** $36   **c.** $46

4. a. $20   **b.** $30   **c.** $40

5. a. $25   **b.** $27   **c.** $29

6. a. $15   **b.** $17   **c.** $19

Activity 2: Wish List

I have about $_____ to spend on _____ items for a community center or for myself. I need to purchase at least five different items.

Here is what I am planning to buy:

Wish List

Items	Prices

1. How did you *estimate* how much everything would cost?

2. How did you find *exactly* how much everything would cost?

3. Are you satisfied with your estimate? Why?

Practice: Nearest Dollar

Rounding numbers makes them more "friendly," or easier to work with. Round up if the number is halfway or more to the next dollar, and round down if the number is less than halfway to the next dollar. For example, $4.25 is rounded down to $4, and $12.80 is rounded up to $13.

Round each amount to the nearest dollar.

Example: $19.50   _____$20_____

1. $10.51   _____

2. $0.50   _____

3. $7.49   _____

4. 39¢   _____

5. $43.50   _____

6. $29.99   _____

7. $99.45   _____

8. $609.77   _____

9. $999.51   _____

Practice: Nearest 10

Sometimes you need to round to the nearest $10 amount. Ask yourself, "Which multiple of 10 is closest to this amount?" If the number is halfway or more to the next multiple of 10, round up. If it is less than halfway, round down.

Round each of the following amounts to the nearest $10.

Example: $19.50   _____$20_____

1. $10.51   _____

2. $82.50   _____

3. $7.49   _____

4. 39¢   _____

5. $43.50   _____

6. $36.04   _____

7. $219.45   _____

8. $604.77   _____

9. $999.15   _____

Practice: Closest Answer

Use rounding and regrouping to find the closest answer to each problem. Circle your choice and then explain your reasoning.

1. $26 + $18.99 + $4

   a. $30   **b.** $50   **c.** $70

2. 10 + 59 − 19

   a. 70   **b.** 60   **c.** 50

3. 79 − 25 + 19

   a. 65   **b.** 75   **c.** 85

4. 86 + 13 + 2

   a. 90   **b.** 100   **c.** 110

5. $24.99 + $9.99 + $11.99

   a. $65   **b.** $55   **c.** $45

Practice: It's about . . .

Use rounding and mental math strategies to estimate the following amounts.

1. **a.** Sharonda is setting tables for a banquet. There are 19 round tables, each seating eight people. She places two forks at each setting, so that's about _____ forks.

   b. Show how you arrived at your estimate.

   c. Is your estimate above or below the actual amount? Explain.

2. **a.** Esteban is contributing to his nephew's birthday party. Eight children will be at the party. He has agreed to purchase two balloons and a party favor for each child. The balloons his nephew wants cost $0.89 each and the party favors are each $3.99. About how much money will Esteban contribute?

   b. Show how you arrived at your estimate.

   c. Is your estimate above or below the actual amount? Explain.

Mental Math Practice: How Much Money Is in the Jar?

1. How much money is in each jar? Using mental math, quickly combine amounts that equal a dollar.

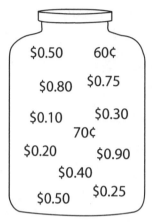

$0.50   60¢

$0.80 $0.75

$0.10 $0.30

70¢

$0.20 $0.90

$0.40

$0.50 $0.25

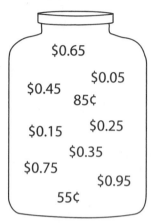

$0.65

$0.05

$0.45

85¢

$0.15 $0.25

$0.35

$0.75

$0.95

55¢

a. Total = _____

b. Total = _____

2. Write down five combinations that make a dollar.

3. Use mental math to add the following amounts:

   a. $0.10 + $0.20 + $0.30 + $0.40 + $0.50 + $0.60 + $0.70 + $0.80 + $0.90 = _____

   b. $0.05 + $0.15 + $0.25 + $0.35 + $0.45 + $0.55 + $0.65 + $0.75 + $0.85 + $0.95 = _____

Mental Math Practice: Bigger Jars of Money

1. How much money is in each jar? Using mental math, quickly combine amounts that equal $10.

$6.00 $7.50
$1.50 $7.00
   $3.50
$4.00
      $2.50
$8.50
$3.00 $6.50

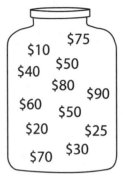

$10 $75
$40 $50
      $80 $90
$60 $50
$20 $25
$70 $30

   a. Total = _____   b. Total = _____

2. Write down five combinations that make $10.

3. Use mental math to add the following amounts:

   a. $1 + $2 + $3 + $4 + $5 + $6 + $7 + $8 + $9 = _____

   b. $10 + $20 + $30 + $40 + $50 + $60 + $70 + $80 + $90 = _____

Extension: Big Bucks Estimates

When political or corporate executives make budget decisions, they often deal with huge numbers—hundreds of thousands, millions, billions, or trillions of dollars. If you were the executive sharing the following figures with your colleagues, what would you offer as an estimated total?

1. This year, for healthcare we have allocated about $2.5 million for needle exchange programs, $9 million for anti-smoking campaigns, $14 million for rehab centers, and $11 million for detox centers. About how much total are we spending on healthcare?

   a. $35 million

   b. $30 million

   c. $40 million

2. How did you make your estimate?

3. For public works, we will need about $879,000 for paving costs, $154,000 for street lights, $53,000 for street line painting, and $627,000 for plowing. If we don't spend more on anything else, we will still need to budget approximately

   a. $1,700,000.

   b. $17,000,000.

   c. $170,000.

4. How did you make your estimate?

Test Practice

For each question, choose the best answer. Use mental math to solve these problems.

1. At his clothing stall in the flea market, Brian sold a suit for $4.95, a sweater for $3.95, and a winter coat for $14.95. Which of the following is closest to the total amount of his sales?

   (1) $20

   (2) $25

   (3) $30

   (4) $35

   (5) $40

2. Mariana has a used furniture stall in the flea market. She sold a desk for $19, two chairs for $7 each, and a table for $18. Which of the following is closest to the total amount of her sales?

   (1) $30

   (2) $35

   (3) $40

   (4) $45

   (5) $50

3. Elm School has a $150 budget for magazines. The selection committee included these publications on their wish list: *Horizons* @ $24.95/year; *Animal Kingdom* @ $19.99/year; *Hot Cars* @ $44/year; and *Style* @ $35.95/year. When the committee shared this list with the librarian, she said,

   (1) "You have about $75 left to spend."

   (2) "You have gone way over the budget."

   (3) "You are just under $100; choose some more magazines."

   (4) "You spent only about half of the budget."

   (5) "You are close to the limit."

4. Alicia borrowed money for lunch from her brother every day last week. He loaned her $7.55 on Monday, $5.40 on Tuesday, $6.75 on Wednesday, $4.25 on Thursday, and $6.50 on Friday. About how much money did Alicia borrow from her brother?

   (1) $28

   (2) $31

   (3) $33

   (4) $34

   (5) $36

5. Wade bought a used bike for $26. When he got it home, he realized it was too small for him. He found someone to buy it from him for $15. Wade did which of the following from buying and selling the bike?

   (1) Lost about $10

   (2) Gained about $10

   (3) Lost about $15

   (4) Gained about $15

   (5) None of the above

6. Emma sold eight hand-knit baby blankets for $10.95 each. Estimate to the nearest dollar how much money Emma made.

Mental Math in the Checkout Line

> *Do you have enough money to cover the cost of your purchases?*

When you are in the grocery store checkout line, you might need to make sure that you have enough money with you to purchase all the things in your cart. How can you do this quickly?

In this lesson, you get precise with your mental math skills as you work with food prices. As you may do in your life outside math class, you will round to the nearest dollar, calculate, and later adjust the numbers to account for the rounding you did in the beginning.

Activity 1: Math in Line

1. On the way home from work yesterday, I stopped at the store and bought two items. One cost $1.89 and the other cost $3.15. While I was waiting at the checkout line, I reached into my wallet and realized I only had a five-dollar bill. Did I have enough money for my purchases? How do you know?

For Problems 2–5, work with a partner. Solve the problems using mental math and then compare your strategies.

2. Sara is in line at the grocery store. She is buying three loaves of bread for $2.98 each. She hands the cashier a $10 bill.

$2.98   **$2.98**   **$2.98**

a. Does she have enough money? How do you know?

b. How could she round and then adjust her answer to figure out exactly how much change she will get?

3. Daniel goes to the pharmacy and buys two boxes of tissues for $2.09 each, including tax. He gives the cashier a $5 bill.

$2.09 $2.09

a. How much change will he get?

b. Show how you figured out your answer.

4. Jerry spent the day shopping, and his last stop was at a discount department store. He bought four shirts at $6.95 each. He had $25 in his wallet.

$6.95 $6.95
    $6.95 $6.95

a. Did he have enough money to pay for the shirts? How do you know?

b. How could he figure out the exact cost of the shirts in his head?

5. Olga made a quick stop at the drug store. She bought two mystery books at $6.99 each and two birthday cards for $2.25 each. Luckily for Olga, there was no tax, because she had only two $10 bills in her wallet.

$6.99 $6.99 $2.25 $2.25

a. What did she have in her wallet after making the purchases?

b. Show how you figured out your answer.

Activity 2: Rounding and Adjusting

1. Fill in the table below. For each of the items to be purchased,

   - Round the amount;

   - Estimate the amount of the purchase;

   - Find the adjusted amount (more or less than actual cost); and

   - Find the exact amount of the purchase. Use appropriate notation.

   The first one has been done for you.

Items to Be Purchased	Rounded Amount for Each Item	Estimate of Purchase	Adjustment + or –		Exact Amount of Purchase
a. 2 items at $21.90 each	$22	$44		10¢	2($22) – 2(10¢) = $44 – $0.20 = $43.80
b. 3 items at $295 each					
c. 7 items at $19.50 each					
d. 6 items at $2.10 each					
e. 5 items at $6.98 each					
f. 8 items at $4.97 each					
g. 5 items at $10.25 each					

2. Which of the problems above was most challenging for you? Why?

Practice: Using Math Notation

Write each of the following using appropriate math notation. The first one has been done for you.

1. Five times seven plus three times six.

   $(5 \times 7) + (3 \times 6)$ or $5(7) + 3(6)$

2. Four times eleven dollars minus four times three cents.

3. Eight times three dollars plus eight times nine cents.

4. Six times twenty dollars minus six times seven cents.

Problems 5 and 6 represent situations involving rounding and adjusting.

Say whether the adjustment is because the amount was rounded *up* or *down*. Explain how you know.

5. $12(\$3) + 12(2¢)$

6. $4(\$32) - 4(12¢)$

Practice: Adjustments

1. Fill in the table below. For each of the items to be purchased,

   - Round the amount;

   - Estimate the amount of the purchase;

   - Find the adjusted amount (more or less than actual cost); and

   - Find the exact amount of the purchase. Use appropriate notation.

   The first one has been done for you.

Items to Be Purchased	Rounded Amount for Each Item	Estimate of Purchase	Adjustment + or –		Exact Amount of Purchase
a. 5 items at $3.95 each	$4	$20		5 x 5¢ or 25¢	$20 – 25¢ = $19.75
b. 7 items at $1.05 each					
c. 2 items at $39 each					
d. 4 items at $2.19 each					
e. 5 items at $6.98 each					
f. 3 items at $9.97 each					

2. Which of the problems above was most challenging for you? Why?

Practice: Exactly

Complete each of the following problems. Show your work.

1. Rachel bought two placemats for $4.07 each. She first made an estimate of $8 for her purchases and then adjusted by _____ to get exactly _____.

2. Liu bought three pies for $5.98 each. He estimated they would cost $18 total and then adjusted by _____ to get exactly _____.

3. Jon bought three cartons of milk for $2.95 each. He paid with a $10 bill. He first estimated his change by subtracting $9 from the $10 and then adjusted by _____ to get exactly _____.

4. Ariel purchased seven packs of paper cups for $2.01 each. She paid with a $20 bill. She first estimated her change by thinking 7 x 2 = 14 and 20 – 14 = 6, and then she adjusted by _____ to get exactly _____.

5. Show how you could solve this problem differently.

Practice: Closer to $50 or $60?

Lilli: "I made almost $60 at the yard sale today! I sold my old sewing machine for $27.99—that's almost $30. Then I sold an old radio for $15—that's almost $20, so I made almost $50 on those two items. I also sold a set of five cups for 99¢ each, so altogether I made almost $60."

Troy: "Actually, you made less than $50. It's easy to find out how much you made—I did it in my head."

1. How could Troy have figured out how much Lilli made?

2. Do you think $60 is a good estimate? Why or why not?

Mental Math Practice: Fast Actions with 10 or 100

> You can add $10 to any amount of money quickly if you keep your eye on the **10's place**.
>
> You can add $100 to any amount quickly if you keep your eye on the **100's place**.

Underline the correct place to focus on in all the amounts. Then add 10 or 100 quickly in your head. Write the result.

Example: If you add $10 to $5<u>6</u>8, you get $ 578

1. If you add $100 to $568, you get _____.

2. If you add $10 to $283, you get _____.

3. If you add $100 to $283, you get _____.

4. If you add $10 to $650, you get _____.

5. If you add $100 to $650, you get _____.

6. If you add $10 to $396, you get _____.

7. If you add $100 to $396, you get _____.

8. If you add $10 to $969, you get _____.

9. If you add $100 to $969, you get _____.

Use the pattern of adding 10 or 100 to fill in the missing amount.

10. $25 + 8 + \underline{\hspace{1cm}} = 35$

11. $67 + \underline{\hspace{1cm}} + 3 = 77$

12. $\underline{\hspace{1cm}} + 40 + 60 = 528$

Mental Math Practice: Fast Actions with 9 or 90

Fill in the missing numbers. Look for a pattern.

1. a. 65 + 10 = _____   **b.** 65 + 9 = _____

2. a. 137 + 10 = _____   **b.** 137 + 9 = _____

3. a. 89 + 10 = _____   **b.** 89 + 9 = _____

4. a. 406 + 10 = _____   **b.** 406 + 9 = _____

5. a. 665 + 10 = _____   **b.** 665 + 9 = _____

6. a. 198 + 10 = _____   **b.** 198 + 9 = _____

7. What is a fast way to add nine to any amount with mental math?

8. a. 650 + 100 = _____   **b.** 650 + 90 = _____

9. a. 437 + 100 = _____   **b.** 437 + 90 = _____

10. a. 809 + 100 = _____   **b.** 809 + 90 = _____

11. a. 916 + 100 = _____   **b.** 916 + 90 = _____

12. What is a fast way to add 90 to any amount with mental math?

Extension: Weekly Totals

Estimate the weekly totals in your head. Tell someone how you made your estimate.

1. It is a good idea to keep track of the hours you work so you know how much money you are owed. Andy kept track of his time as follows:

Week of Feb 7–11	
Day	**Time**
Monday	5 hr., 15 min.
Tuesday	7 hr.
Wednesday	3 hr., 45 min.
Thursday	7 hr., 10 min.
Friday	5 hr., 15 min.

   a. About how many hours did Andy work?

   b. Explain how you used mental math to figure out your answer.

2. Mark keeps track of the number of miles he jogs each day. Last week, he jogged six days:

Exercise	
Day	**Miles Jogged**
Sunday	3.1 mi.
Monday	3.8 mi.
Tuesday	3 mi.
Wednesday	4.2 mi.
Thursday	2.7 mi.
Friday	4 mi.

a. About how many miles did Mark jog last week?

b. Explain how you figured out the number of miles that Mark jogged.

1. If you purchased the following items, about how much change would you get if you paid with a $50 bill?

   Sneakers—$39.95

   Hat—$4.95

   Socks—$2.99

   (1) A little less than $4

   (2) A little more than $3

   (3) A little less than $3

   (4) A little more than $2

   (5) A little less than $2

2. Bella gave the store clerk $20 for three jerseys she bought. The jerseys cost $6.99, $8.95, and $14.99. The clerk asked her for more money. How much more did she ask for?

   (1) Another $10

   (2) Another $11

   (3) Another $20

   (4) Another $5

   (5) Another $1

3. Pierre is saving money to take his girlfriend to dinner and a show for her birthday. Dinner at her favorite restaurant will cost $60. Tickets for the show are $43.89 each (tax included). Exactly how much money does Pierre need to save?

   (1) $105

   (2) $143

   (3) $147.78

   (4) $147.89

   (5) $148.89

4. Frank bought several tools at the Kitchen Warehouse, paying these prices: spatula, $3.95; whisk, $2.99; bowl, $7.29; and platter, $40.79. He rounded and estimated the total cost to be $55. Frank rounded to which of the following set of numbers?

   (1) $4 + $2 + $7 + $40

   (2) $4 + $3 + $7 + $41

   (3) $4 + $3 + $8 + $41

   (4) $4 + $2 + $7 + $41

   (5) $4 + $3 + $8 + $40

5. Which of the following adjustments did Frank need to make to get an exact answer?

   (1) Add $1.04 to his estimate.

   (2) Add $1.14 to his estimate.

   (3) Add $1.08 and subtract $0.06 from his estimate.

   (4) Add $0.29 and subtract $0.27 from his estimate.

   (5) Add $0.56 to his estimate.

6. Elisa's favorite soda is on sale at $0.89 per liter (including the deposit). How much will eight liters of soda cost Elisa?

Traveling with Numbers

Have you ever driven across the United States?

Large numbers challenge our imaginations. To make sense of large numbers, it helps to have a feel for how big 10,000, 1,000, and 100 really are.

How far is 3,000 miles? How tall is the highest mountain? How can you compare different amounts of money? How can you use numbers to organize files in an office?

This lesson will ask you to think about the size of large numbers and to round, order, and compare them. You will use the **number line** as a thinking tool.

Activity 1: How Many Miles to Boston?

Interstate 90 (I-90) is the longest highway in the United States. It extends across the country from Seattle, Washington, to Boston, Massachusetts, crossing 13 states for a total of about 3,000 miles (3,112 miles to be more exact).

1. Look at the map of the United States. I-90 is highlighted. How many states does I-90 cross?

2. Look at the length of I-90 in each state on the map. Which state do you think will take the longest time to cross? Which will take the shortest time?

3. Which state do you think you will be in when you are about halfway from Seattle to Boston? Mark the halfway point on the map.

4. Use the number line below to think about a cross-country trip from Seattle to Boston. You should plan to travel about 300 miles a day.

   a. On the number line, show the 300-mile jumps. Label the numbers at each jump.

   b. Approximately how many days will your trip take?

Interstate 90 on a
Map of the United States

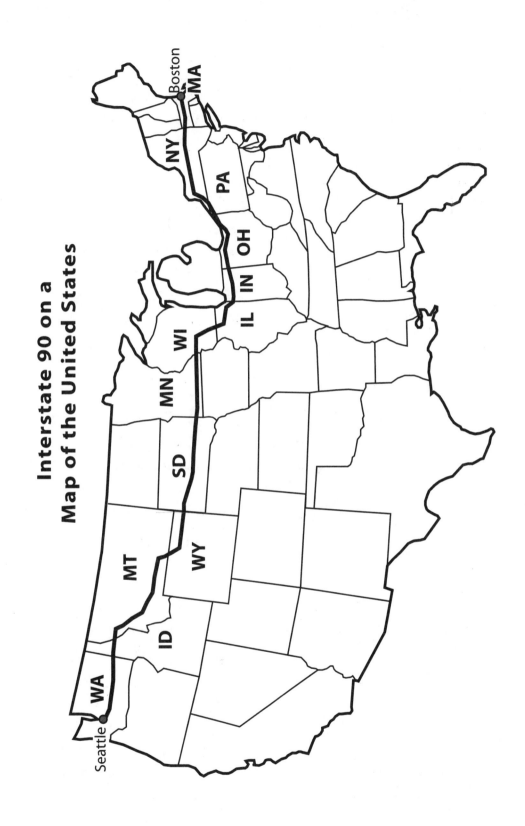

Activity 2: Planning Where to Stay

On the facing page is a chart that shows cities along I-90 and their distances in miles from Seattle.

1. Use the chart to decide where you will stay for the night. Remember: You want to travel about 300 miles a day. On the chart, circle the towns where you will stay. The first stop has been chosen for you. You decide on the other stops along the way.

2. Now write the towns where you decided to stay and their distance from Seattle on the I-90 number line below. The first one has been done for you.

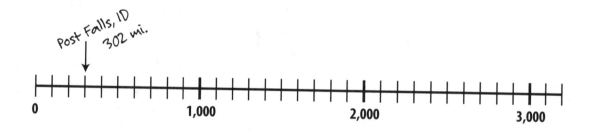

Travel Data for I-90

Seattle, WA (Jct I-5)—0	Sundance, WY—1,111	Rockford, IL—2,020
Mercer Island, WA—5	Spearfish, SD—1,143	Belvidere, IL—2,029
Bellevue, WA—8	Sturgis, SD—1,161	Elgin, WI—2,059
Issaquah, WA—15	Rapid City, SD—1,189	O'Hare Airport, IL—2,082
Easton, WA—69	Box Elder, SD—1,196	Junction I-94, IL—2,089
Cle Elum, WA—82	Wall, SD—1,242	Chicago, IL—2,097
Ellensburg, WA—108	Kadoka, SD—1,282	Junction I-94—2,104
Kittitas, WA—114	Murdo, SD—1,323	Hammond, IN—2,119
Moses Lake, WA—174	Jct I-83, SD—1,340	Gary, IN—2,126
Sprague, WA—243	Presho, SD—1,357	Portage, IN—2,136
Spokane, WA—280	Kennebec, SD—1,367	South Bend, IN—2,189
Greenacres, WA—293	Chamberlain, SD—1,395	Elkhart, IN (I-80)—2,179
Post Falls, ID—302	Plankinton, SD—1,440	Junction 169—2,231
Coeur d'Alene, ID—310	Mitchell, SD—1,462	Toledo, OH— 2,309
Kellogg, ID—348	Hartford, SD—1,519	Lorain, OH—2,387
Wallace, ID—359	Sioux Falls, SD—1,530	Cleveland, OH—2,415
Superior, MT—418	Luverne, MN—1,556	Euclid, OH—2,430
Alberton, MT—446	Worthington, MN—1,588	Madison, OH—2,458
Missoula, MT—475	Jackson, MN—1,618	Conneaut, OH—2,486
Drummond, MT—525	Fairmont, MN—1,646	Erie, PA—2,513
Deer Lodge, MT—555	Albert Lea, MN—1,702	Junction I-86, PA—2,525
Butte, MT—593	Austin, MN—1,722	Buffalo, NY—2,605
Whitehall, MT—626	Rochester, MN—1,753	Rochester, NY—2,669
Bozeman, MT—678	St. Charles, MN—1,776	Syracuse, NY—2,748
Columbus, MT—778	La Crosse, WI—1,823	Utica, NY—2,799
Billings, MT—821	Sparta, WI—1,845	Amsterdam, NY—2,858
Junction I-94, MT—826	Junction I-94, WI—1,864	Schenectady, NY—2,878
Hardin, MT—865	Mauston, WI—1,889	Albany, NY—2,886
Crow Agency, MT—879	Wisconsin Dells, WI—1,904	W. Springfield, MA— 2,968
Sheridan, WY—947	Junction I-39, WI—1,925	Worcester, MA—3,016
Buffalo, WY—981	Madison, WI—1,955	Junction I-95—3,045
Gillette, WY—1,050	Janesville, WI—1,988	Boston, MA—3,056
Moorcroft, WY—1,078	Beloit, WI—2,002	

3. Will you spend more than one night in any state? Which one(s)?

4. Which town is closest to the halfway mark?

5. How many nights will you spend traveling across the country?

6. Did you use rounding and mental calculations to arrive at your answers? How?

Activity 3: Rounding Distances

The number 3,000 is a "friendlier" number than 3,112; the number 300 is easier to think about than 298; and 50 is easier to work with than 47. We often round numbers to friendlier ones so we can work with them in our heads.

1. **a.** Round each of distances of I-90 in the 13 states to the closest number ending in zero (to the nearest 10). List the new numbers in the chart.

State	I-90 Distance (in miles)	Rounded to the Nearest Ten Miles	Rounded to the Nearest 100 Miles
Washington	298		
Idaho	73		
Montana	558		
Wyoming	207		
South Dakota	412		
Minnesota	275		
Wisconsin	188		
Illinois	103		
Indiana	157		
Ohio	244		
Pennsylvania	47		
New York	391		
Massachusetts	159		
Total	3,112		

Source: Distances rounded to the nearest mile. Obtained from information provided on the Web site http://www.ihoz.com/I90.html.

b. How did you decide whether to round up or down?

2. Add the numbers you listed in Problem 1a. Show how you grouped the numbers to add them. How close is your estimated answer to 3,112?

3. a. Now round your numbers to the nearest 100. List the new numbers in the chart. After rounding, add the numbers without a calculator. Show how you grouped the numbers this time. What is the sum?

b. Compare your total miles for Problem 3a to the total you estimated for Problem 1a and to 3,112 miles. What can you say about rounding numbers?

Tips on Rounding

To round to the nearest 100: If the number of 10's amounts to less than 50, round down to the next lowest hundred.

Examples:

936	900
309	300
442	400

If the number of 10's amounts to 50 or more, round up to the next highest hundred.

Examples:

589	600
672	700
169	200

Practice: High and Not So High Peaks

The mountains listed here are in alphabetical order.

Bradbury Mountain in the United States	485 ft.
Cadillac Mountain in the United States	1,532 ft.
Kilimanjaro in Tanzania	19,340 ft.
Mt. Apo in the Phillippines	9,692 ft.
Mt. Cook in New Zealand	12,349 ft.
Mt. David in the United States	48 ft.
Mt. Etna in Italy	10,902 ft.
Pico Duarte in the Dominican Republic	10,417 ft.

1. List the mountains and their corresponding heights in order from lowest to highest.

   Mountain Name **Height (in feet)**

   a. _____ _____

   b. _____ _____

   c. _____ _____

   d. _____ _____

   e. _____ _____

   f. _____ _____

   g. _____ _____

   h. _____ _____

2. Label the number line from 0 to 20,000 by thousands. What is the midpoint? Locate at least four of the mountains on the number line.

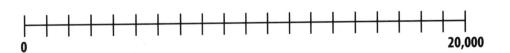

0   20,000

3. What is the height of Mt. David rounded to the nearest 100 feet?

4. Do some research: What is the highest mountain in the country where you were born? How high is it?

Everyday Number Sense: Mental Math and Visual Models   EMPower™

Practice: Checks—Say It in Words

The six checks on this and the following page were received at a used car dealership.

1. What is the total take for the day? Explain your reasoning.

   a. Estimated amount:

   b. Exact amount:

2. Write the amount of each check in words.

   Example:

   Date: _____

   Pay to the
   Order of: _____ | $7,714.00 |

   ___Seven thousand seven hundred fourteen and $^{00}/_{100}$___ **Dollars**

   Memo: _____ _____

   a.

   Date: _____

   Pay to the
   Order of: _____ | $4,709.00 |

   _____ **Dollars**

   Memo: _____ _____

b.

Date: _____

Pay to the
Order of: _____ $3,081.00

_____ **Dollars**

Memo: _____

c.

Date: _____

Pay to the
Order of: _____ $10,001.00

_____ **Dollars**

Memo: _____

d.

Date: _____

Pay to the
Order of: _____ $10,010.00

_____ **Dollars**

Memo: _____

e.

Date: _____

Pay to the
Order of: _____ $10,100.00

_____ **Dollars**

Memo: _____

Practice: More Check Writing

1. Write the amount for each of the following checks using numbers.

a.

Date: _____

Pay to the
Order of: _____ [ ]

Nine thousand six hundred fifty-three and ⁰⁰/₁₀₀ ___ **Dollars**

Memo: _____

b.

Date: _____

Pay to the
Order of: _____ [ ]

Two thousand ninety-seven and ⁰⁰/₁₀₀ ___ **Dollars**

Memo: _____

c.

Date: _____

Pay to the
Order of: _____ [ ]

Eight thousand eight and ⁰⁰/₁₀₀ ___ **Dollars**

Memo: _____

d.

Date: _____

**Pay to the
Order of:** _____ [ ]

_____Five thousand one hundred six and $^{00}/_{100}$_____ **Dollars**

Memo: _____ _____

e.

Date: _____

**Pay to the
Order of:** _____ [ ]

_____Nine thousand twenty and $^{00}/_{100}$_____ **Dollars**

Memo: _____ _____

Practice: Filing

Shown here are pictures of some file cabinet drawers and files to go in them. Look at the account numbers on each file, find the drawer where it belongs, and write the account number below that drawer. The first file has been done for you.

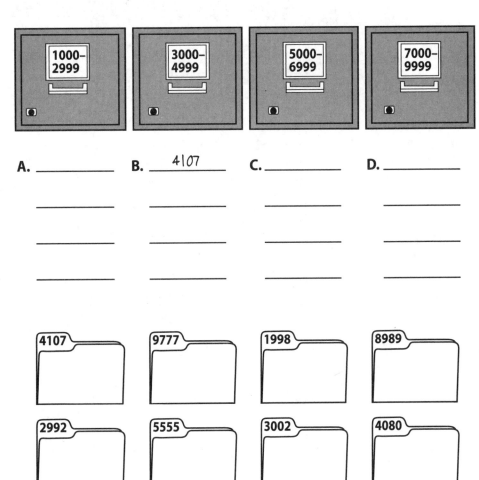

| 1000–2999 | 3000–4999 | 5000–6999 | 7000–9999 |

A. _____   B. __4107__   C. _____   D. _____

_____   _____   _____   _____

_____   _____   _____   _____

_____   _____   _____   _____

4107   9777   1998   8989

2992   5555   3002   4080

Practice: More Filing

This time the drawers are set up differently. Write the account number of the file below the drawer where it belongs. The first file has been done for you.

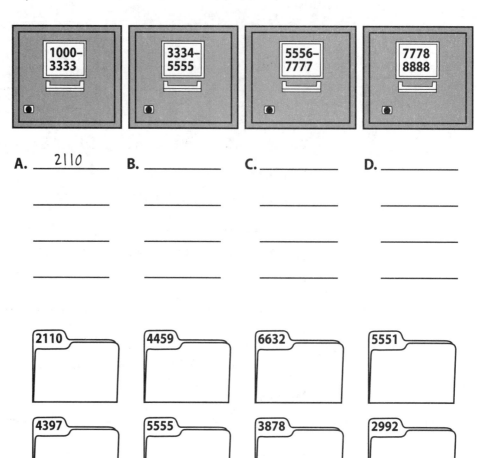

1000–3333	3334–5555	5556–7777	7778 8888

A. ___2110___ B. _____ C. _____ D. _____

_____ _____ _____ _____

_____ _____ _____ _____

_____ _____ _____ _____

2110   4459   6632   5551

4397   5555   3878   2992

Mental Math Practice: Doubles

Many numbers are easy to double, but some take special attention.

Double each of these numbers in your head. Write the result under the number.

1. 0   1   2   3   4   5   6   7   8   9   10

Double

_____

2. 10   20   30   40   50   60   70   80   90   100

Double

_____

3. 12   21   33   44   51   62   73   84   92   103

Double

_____

4. 5   15   25   35   45   55   65   75   85   95   105

Double

_____

5. 16   27   38   49   56   67   78   89   96   107

Double

_____

6. What patterns do you see?

Mental Math Practice: Triples

It is useful to be able to triple amounts.

Triple each of these numbers in your head. Write the result under the number.

1. 0   1   2   3   4   5   6   7   8   9   10

Triple

_____

2. 10   20   30   40   50   60   70   80   90   100

Triple

_____

3. 12   21   33   44   51   62   73   84   92   103

Triple

_____

4. 5   15   25   35   45   55   65   75   85   95   105

Triple

_____

5. 16   27   38   49   56   67   78   89   96   107

Triple

_____

6. What patterns do you see?

1. Which is the third number in order from smallest to largest in this list?

   1,021   10,257   5,703   9,982   5,730

   (1) 1,021

   (2) 5,703

   (3) 5,730

   (4) 9,982

   (5) 10,257

2. Which number is less than 100 away from 5,200?

   (1) 5,090

   (2) 5,100

   (3) 5,290

   (4) 5,390

   (5) 5,490

3. Millie wrote a check for $1,018. Which of the following shows the number written correctly?

   (1) One thousand eight dollars and 00/100

   (2) One thousand eighteen dollars and 00/100

   (3) One thousand one hundred eight dollars and 00/100

   (4) Ten thousand eight dollars and 00/100

   (5) Ten hundred eighteen dollars and 00/100

4. Which of the following would not be a filing mistake?

   (1) Account 5456 filed between 5004 and 5400

   (2) Account 5456 filed between 5450 and 6000

   (3) Account 5456 filed between 500 and 600

   (4) Account 5456 filed between 5500 and 6000

   (5) Account 5456 filed between 500 and 5000

5. Jena lives in Bourne on Cape Cod. She and her friend decide to bike to Boston. They start early and bike for 36 miles before taking their first break. They bike another 19 miles and take another break. The distance between Bourne and Boston is 71 miles. How much farther do Jena and her friend have to bike to get to Boston?

   (1) 11 miles

   (2) 16 miles

   (3) 21 miles

   (4) 41 miles

   (5) 126 miles

6. Jon and Zach are sharing the driving on a cross-country road trip. When Zach took the wheel yesterday morning, they were at mile 347. At the end of the day, they were at mile 720. How far did Zach drive?

Traveling in Time

How long ago was that?

Number lines help you compare numbers and visualize how far apart they are.

In this lesson you will use a number line to travel back and forth in time.

Thinking about 1's, 10's, 100's and 1,000's makes counting and comparing easier, and you can do this in your head. Comparing numbers can save you time and money, help you make decisions, and increase your skill at choosing the right answers on a test.

Activity 1: Birthday Numbers

1. Use the following number line to find the birth year of someone 36 years old. Then write down, step by step, what you did in your head.

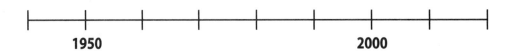

2. **a.** Use the number line to find the birth year of someone 48 years old. Then write down your steps.

   b. How could using the answer to Problem 1 help you solve Problem 2?

3. Use the number line to determine the age of a person born in 1949. Write down your steps.

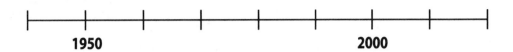

1950   2000

4. Use the number line to show your age. Write down your steps.

1950   2000

Activity 2: How Long Ago?

Listed here are some events that had a huge effect on the course of history in the United States. How long ago did each event happen? Number lines will help you figure out the answers.

Choose two or three events. Using the number lines provided,

- Fill in the missing numbers;

- Label the year of the event you chose and the current year;

- Find the difference in years between the event and the current year;

- Write an **equation** (or equations) that show(s) what you did.

1. 1860—United States Civil War Starts

The North (the Union) fought the South (the Confederacy) over states' rights and the right to own slaves.

a.

1860 1870 [   ] 1890 1900 [   ] 1920 1930 1940 1950 1960 [   ] 1980 [   ] [   ] 2010 2020

b. The U.S. Civil War started _____ years ago.

c. Equation(s) for my method of solving the problem:

2. 1903—First Flight

The Wright Brothers flew the first plane in Kittyhawk, North Carolina. They built the plane and its engine in their bicycle shop. They flew three times that first day. Their final flight went a distance of 852 feet and lasted 59 seconds.

a.

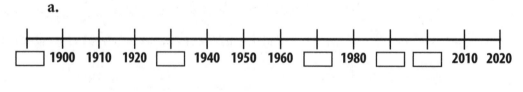

[   ] 1900 1910 1920 [   ] 1940 1950 1960 [   ] 1980 [   ] [   ] 2010 2020

b. The first powered flight was _____ years ago.

c. Equation(s) for my method of solving the problem:

3. 1906—San Francisco Earthquake

In San Francisco, California, the nation's worst earthquake killed more than 500 people. It caused a huge fire which destroyed homes and stores across the entire city.

a.

b. The San Francisco Earthquake occurred _____ years ago.

c. Equation(s) for my method of solving the problem:

4. 1918—The Great Flu Epidemic

A deadly flu epidemic swept across the United States, killing 500,000 Americans, young and old.

a.

b. The Great Flu Epidemic took place _____ years ago.

c. Equation(s) for my method of solving the problem:

5. 1920—Women Granted the Right to Vote

The Eighteenth Amendment to the Constitution passed, giving women over the age of 21 the right to vote. (The Constitution gave white men the right to vote 144 years earlier; the Fifteenth Amendment gave black men the right to vote 50 years earlier.)

a.

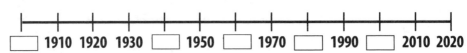

b. Women were granted the right to vote _____ years ago.

c. Equation(s) for my method of solving the problem:

6. 1929—The Stock Market Crash

The United States stock market crashed on October 9, 1929, because there was no real money to back up all the financial deals people were making on paper. The crash caused banks and businesses to fail, and millions of people were put out of work. It was the beginning of the Great Depression.

a.

b. The stock market crash occurred _____ years ago.

c. Equation(s) for my method of solving the problem:

7. 1935—The "Dust Bowl"

In 1935, after years of little or no rain, the farmland in the central part of the United States turned to dust. On a day called Black Sunday, a strong wind blew the dust into gigantic black clouds of dirt that covered everything, turning day into night. With their farms ruined, many farmers and their families took what little they had and left their land. Many ended up in California, where millions of people with no jobs lined up every day in soup lines for something to eat.

a.

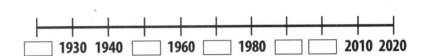

b. Black Sunday happened _____ years ago.

c. Equation(s) for my method of solving the problem:

8. 1945—World War II Ends

World War II began in 1939, when Germany, led by Hitler, invaded other countries in Europe. The dictators in Italy and Japan joined forces with Hitler; Britain and France declared war on Germany. Before the war was over, 25 countries across the world, including the United States, were involved. More than 52 million people died in fighting, in concentration camps, and from atomic bombs dropped on Japan. The war ended in 1945, when Germany and Japan surrendered.

a.

b. World War II ended _____ years ago.

c. Equation(s) for my method of solving the problem:

9. 1957—Russians Launch Sputnik

The Russians were the first to send a satellite, named Sputnik, into space. Sputnik was the size of a basketball and circled the sun every 98 minutes. From Earth, you could see it crossing the sky. Sputnik collected information about space and sent it back to Earth.

a.

b. Sputnik was launched _____ years ago.

c. Equation(s) for my method of solving the problem:

10. 1963—President John F. Kennedy Assassinated

John F. Kennedy, the 34th President of the United States, was shot and killed in Dallas, Texas. (The next day, his supposed assassin, Lee Harvey Oswald, was shot and killed by a visitor to the jail where Oswald was being held.)

a.

b. President Kennedy was shot and killed _____ years ago.

c. Equation(s) for my method of solving the problem:

11. 1968—Civil Rights Act Passed

Discrimination on the basis of race, creed (religion or beliefs), or country of origin was outlawed by the U.S. federal government in 1968.

a.

1950 ☐ 1970 ☐ ☐ 2000 2010 ☐

b. The Civil Rights Act became law _____ years ago.

c. Equation(s) for my method of solving the problem:

12. 1975—The Vietnam War Ends

The United States traveled across the world to fight a war in Vietnam to stop the spread of Communism. The war became very unpopular; thousands of people thought the United States should not have interfered. For the first time in history, public opinion caused the United States to withdraw from a war.

a.

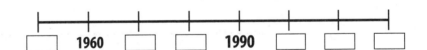

☐ 1960 ☐ ☐ 1990 ☐ ☐ ☐

b. The Vietnam War ended _____ years ago.

c. Equation(s) for my method of solving the problem:

Practice: Use Up the Space—Plan Well

Creating a number line takes planning. Fit the numbers on a line so they are evenly spaced. Use a ruler to help you figure the spacing.

1. Make a 0–8 number line. Mark the line and label the whole numbers 1–7.

0   8

2. Make a 0–10 number line. Mark the line and label the whole numbers 1–9.

0   10

3. Make a 0–20 number line. Mark and label the multiples of five. Fit the numbers on the line. Leave equal space between them.

0   20

4. Make a 0–100 number line. Mark and label the multiples of ten.

0   100

5. Make a 0–500 number line. Choose which numbers to mark and label.

0   500

6. Make a 0–1,000 number line. Mark and label the multiples of 100.

0   1,000

Practice: On the Number Line

Use the number lines provided to situate all the distances in each problem.

1. The Superwoman Bike Ride is 110 miles from start to finish. Josey has ridden 33 miles, Tim is 19 miles ahead of her, and Tia is 12 miles behind Tim. Anna is 34 miles ahead of Tia. How far along is everyone? Mark their places on the number line.

2. Francisco and his brothers and sisters all live within 100 miles of each other.

   • His sister Elsa lives the farthest west.

   • Esmeralda lives 23 miles east of Elsa.

   • Andres lives 11 miles east of Esmeralda.

   • Susana is 32 miles east of Andres.

   • Francisco lives the farthest east.

   How many miles are between Susana's home and Francisco's?

Mental Math Practice: Count Up and Down by 10's

Fill in the columns, counting up or down by 10's, starting with the number at the top.

The first row has been done for you.

Count Up by 10, Starting at. . .			Count Down by 10, Starting at. . .	
27	365	619	315	203
37	375	629	305	193

Mental Math Practice: By What Did I Count?

Look at the pattern. Find the missing number.

1. 63, 73, _____, 93, 103

   By what did I count?

2. 40, 70, _____, 130, 160

   By what did I count?

3. 114, 214, 314, _____

   By what did I count?

4. 250, 240, _____, 220

   By what did I count back?

5. 377, 337, _____, 257

   By what did I count back?

6. 1,006, _____, 986, 976

   By what did I count back?

7. 1,006, _____, 806, 706

   By what did I count back?

Extension: Life Line

Every life is full of significant events that make up our personal history.

1. Mark the number line with your birth year and the current year.

$$\vdash\!\!\!-\!\!\!-\!\!\!-\!\!\!-\!\!\!-\!\!\!-\!\!\!-\!\!\!-\!\!\!-\!\!\!-\!\!\!-\!\!\!-\!\!\!-\!\!\!-\!\!\!-\!\!\!-\!\!\!\dashv$$

2. Use the following time line to show two important events in your life such as these:

   First year of school
   First job
   First child
   Year your grandmother was born
   Year when you moved
   Year when you received your driver's license
   Important events in your country

   (Use a separate piece of paper if you prefer to make a longer line.)

$$\vdash\!\!\!-\!\!\!-\!\!\!-\!\!\!-\!\!\!-\!\!\!-\!\!\!-\!\!\!-\!\!\!-\!\!\!-\!\!\!-\!\!\!-\!\!\!-\!\!\!-\!\!\!-\!\!\!-\!\!\!\dashv$$

3. Use a different colored marker for each event, and show how many years ago each event occurred. Then fill in the information in the following sentences and write equations for each event that show your thinking.

   a. _____ years ago, I _____.

      My equation(s) for how I figured out how long ago this event took place:

   b. _____ years ago, I _____.

      My equation(s) for how I figured out how long ago this event took place:

Test Practice

1. Vienna prepared 125 box lunches on Monday and 205 on Tuesday. Which equation corresponds to the jumps shown on the number line?

   (1) $125 + 75 = 205$

   (2) $75 + 5 = 80$

   (3) $25 + 75 = 100$

   (4) $125 + 100 = 225$

   (5) $205 - 100 = 125$

2. The Sunshine Library is trying to raise $750 for a new television and DVD player. According to the sign, how much more do they need to raise?

   (1) $225

   (2) $275

   (3) $325

   (4) $350

   (5) $375

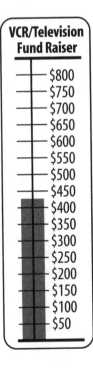

3. Charlie is a bus driver. His route is along Main Street. A passenger gets on at 38th Street and asks Charlie how many more blocks there are to 59th Street. Charlie says,

   (1) 48, 58, 59; that is 3 blocks.

   (2) 38, 48, 58, 59; that is 4 blocks.

   (3) 48, 58, 59; that is 11 blocks.

   (4) 38, 48, 58, 59; that is 21 blocks.

   (5) 38, 48, 58, 59; that is 31 blocks.

4. Which of the following number lines shows what Charlie said?

   (1)

   (2)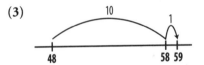

   (3)

   (4)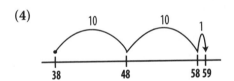

   (5)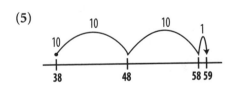

5. Construction on the Roman Colosseum started in 72 AD and was finished in 80 AD. In 2005, a visitor calculated the number of years ago it was finished. How many years ago was that?

   (1) 1,035

   (2) 1,925

   (3) 1,933

   (4) 2,025

   (5) 2,033

6. In 1876, Alexander Graham Bell invented the telephone. The modern cellphone has been available since 1991. How many years were between the invention of the telephone and the availability of the cellphone?

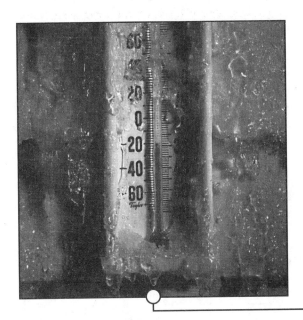

Extending the Line

What do you wear when the temperature drops below zero?

You have worked with a number line to locate, compare, and find **differences** between numbers. The numbers were all **positive numbers**, greater than zero. In this lesson, you will work with **negative numbers**, numbers that are less than zero.

Businesses operating "in the red," budget deficits, and temperatures dropping below zero are examples of situations involving negative numbers. Tune into the nightly news, and listen for finance and science reports. Do you hear negative numbers being used? By thinking of negative numbers along a number line, you can visualize the information in those news reports.

Activity 1: In the Red

Many people have bounced a check at one time or another. The check "bounces" when there is not enough money in the account to cover the amount of the check; in such a case, the account has a negative balance.

Work with a partner to track the daily balance in George's checking account:

- Make a number line.

- Use a red pencil to write the numbers when George was "in the red," or below zero.

- Use a black marker to write the numbers when George was "in the black," or above zero.

- Write the date next to each balance on the number line.

1. January 26: George had $100 in the bank. He paid the gas bill of $175.

    His balance was _____.

2. January 30: George deposited his $950 paycheck.

    His balance was _____.

3. February 2: George paid his rent of $725.

    His balance was _____.

4. February 16: George paid off his credit card balance, $450.

    His balance was _____.

5. February 24: George transferred $800 from savings to checking.

    His balance was _____.

6. Did George have enough money in the bank to pay off his $650 car loan? Explain.

Activity 2: Record Highs, Record Lows

Temperatures vary all over the world. Around the equator, temperatures stay very warm, while at the North and South Poles, temperatures are always quite cold. Some other places in the world experience extreme temperatures.

Part 1

Locate the following temperatures given in degrees Fahrenheit (°F) on the thermometer.

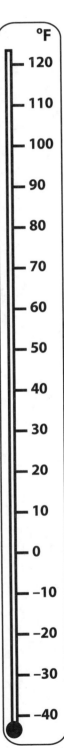

1. Today's temperature:

2. Record high temperature in July 1995 in Phoenix, Arizona: 121°F

3. Record low temperature in January 1905 in Arkansas: −29°F

4. The warmest temperature you have ever experienced:

5. The coldest temperature you have ever experienced:

6. What is the difference between the warmest and coldest temperatures you have experienced? Explain how you found your answer.

7. How would you describe 0°F?

Part 2

The following chart shows record high and low temperatures from each of Earth's continents.

Continent	Highest Recorded Temperature (°F)	Lowest Recorded Temperature (°F)
Europe	Sevilla, Spain 122°	Ust-Scugor, U.S.S.R. −67°
Asia	Tirat Zevi, Israel 129°	Ojmjakon & Verkhoyansk, U.S.S.R. −90°
Africa	Al 'Aziziyah, Libya 136°	Ifrane, Morocco −11°
North America	Death Valley, U.S. 134°	Northrice, Greenland −87°
South America	Rivadavia, Argentina 120°	Sarmiento, Argentina −27°
Australia	Cloncurry, Australia 128°	Charlotte Pass, Australia −8°
Antarctica	Vanda Station 59°	Vostok −129°
World	Al 'Aziziyah, Libya 136°	Vostok −129°

8. What is the highest recorded temperature?

9. What is the lowest recorded temperature?

10. On the following number line, locate the highest and lowest recorded temperatures from all the entries shown on the chart.

11. What is the difference between the highest and lowest recorded temperatures?

   a. Less than 250°F

   b. Equal to 250°F

   c. More than 250°F

12. Find the exact difference and write equations that explain your answer.

13. Choose two temperatures from the chart. Locate and label (by continent) the temperatures on the number line. Then find the difference between the two temperatures you chose.

|———|

Show and explain how you found the difference.

14. Write one thing you noticed about finding the difference between any two temperatures.

Practice: Planting Zones

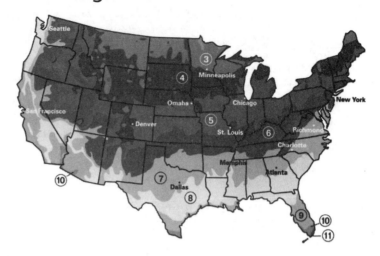

Chart of Plant Hardiness Zones

This chart is used to match the survival temperatures of a plant that you plan to buy with the coldest temperatures in the zone where you live, so that you can be assured that your plant will survive the coldest months in your area.

Zone	Range of Average Annual *Minimum* Temperatures
Zone 3	–40°F to –30°F
Zone 4	–30°F to –20°F
Zone 5	–20°F to –10°F
Zone 6	–10°F to 0°F
Zone 7	0°F to 10°F
Zone 8	10°F to 20°F
Zone 9	20°F to 30°F
Zone 10	30°F to 40°F

1. Mark the **range** of average annual minimum temperatures in all zones on the following number line.

2. How much colder is the *lowest* minimum temperature in Zone 4 (most of the Northeast) than the lowest minimum temperature in Zone 9 (Florida)? Use a number line to check your answer, and Mark Zone 4 and Zone 9 on your U.S. map.

Plant Scenarios—Will the Plants Survive the Winter?

3. Daffodils grow in the spring and are very hardy. They even grow in Zone 3. Minnesota is in Zone 3. During a winter cold spell in northern Minnesota, the temperature rose to 5°F and then dropped 50° at night for several days. Did the daffodils survive this unusual cold spell? Why or why not?

4. A flower catalogue advertised azalea shrubs that were hardy in Zones 6–9. All of Kentucky is Zone 6. One winter, the month of January was very cold. The daytime temperatures hovered around 35°F, and at night, the temperatures dropped nearly 40 degrees. Would the plants be likely to survive? Why or why not?

Practice: What's the Range?

Following are several situations that involve ranges of measurement. Figure out the difference between the high and low in each range. A number line can help you.

1. A typical oven dial looks like this:

    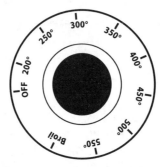

    Most cookies are baked at temperatures between 200°F and 375°F—that's the range for cookie-baking temperatures. What single number best describes the range?

2. Kilowatt hours (kwh) of electricity used are read off a meter that looks like this:

    If the most electricity you ever use in a month is about 877 kwh and the least about 695 kwh, what is the range of your kilowatt hour use? Make your own number line to show how you can calculate the single number that best describes the range.

3. Heights in Amber's class range from 4'10" to 6'2". What is the single number that describes the range of heights in Amber's class? (1 foot = 12")

Practice: Ordering Numbers

The following list shows the checking account balances for several customers of Acme Bank and Trust Co.

Sue: $142   Zoe: –$10   Aaron: –$125   Alice: $5

Kim: –$53   Tad: $269   Lee: $0   Sean: –$79

Devon: –$5   Cally: $1,000   Tanya: –$490   Ollie: –$850

1. Locate each of the balances on the following number line.

```
|——————————————————————————————————————|
```

2. Find the difference between the highest and the lowest balance (the range).

3. A bank clerk has been asked to put the accounts in order from least to greatest balances. Use your labels on the number line in Problem 1 to make the list.

a. _____   g. _____

b. _____   h. _____

c. _____   i. _____

d. _____   j. _____

e. _____   k. _____

f. _____   l. _____

Mental Math Practice: Count Up and Down by 10's

Fill in the columns, counting up or down by 10's, starting with the number at the top.

The first row has been done for you.

Count Up by 10, Starting at. . .			Count Down by 10, Starting at. . .		
–100	**–75**	**–11**	**27**	**123**	2,045
–90	–65	–1	17	113	2,035

Extension: Sorry, Account Overdrawn

Use the numbers and words in the box at the bottom of the page to complete the story.

deposit - money you put in the bank
withdrawal - money you take out or drawn on with a check
balance - amount in your account

ACME Bank

ACME Bank & Trust Company
Est. 1890
500 Riverview Street
Whitehurst, Iowa

Dear Sir or Madam:

It has come to our attention that your account is now overdrawn for the amount of _____. During the past weeks, you made several _____, but also several _____ (reflecting the checks you wrote).

You had a _____ of $500 in your checking account at the start of the month. You then made four deposits, each for $100, giving you a new balance of _____. However, you wrote _____ checks for $200 each, which means you made withdrawals totaling _____. This left you with a net balance of _____ (the amount you are overdrawn).

It is our duty to inform you when you have overdrawn your account and show a negative balance. We are sure you are aware of bank policy regarding overdrawn accounts: We impose a one-time charge of $50 plus $15 for each check you bounce.

Therefore, because two of your checks bounced, we will be placing an additional total charge on your account of _____. Please note this deduction in your checkbook. We trust you will be making a deposit soon to cover these charges and the overdrawn amount.

Sincerely,
Hedley Snobington, Bank President

---

balance	$900	withdrawals	$80
$1,200	deposits	–$300	6	–$300

Extension: Below Sea Level

Continent	Highest Elevation (feet)	Lowest Elevation (feet)
Europe	Gora Elbrus, Russia 18,510'	Caspian Sea, Ukraine/Iran −92'
Asia	Everest, China/Nepal 29,028'	Dead Sea, Israel/Jordan −1,322'
Africa	Kilimanjaro, Tanzania 19,340'	Lac Assal, Djibouti −509'
North America	Mt. McKinley, U.S. 20,320'	Death Valley, U.S. −282'
South America	Cerro Aconcagua, Argentina 22,835'	Salinas Chicas −138'
Australia	Mt. Wilhelm, New Guinea 14,793'	Lake Eyre, Australia −39'
Antarctica	Vinson Massif 11,606'	Sea level

Use the above chart and the number line at right to help with the following questions.

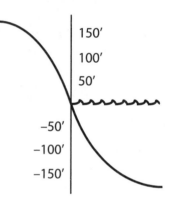

1. The difference in elevation between the lowest point in North America and the lowest point in South America is _____'.

2. The difference in elevation between the highest point in Africa and the highest point in North America is _____'.

3. The difference in elevation between the highest point in the world and the lowest point in the world is about _____'. (Approximate to the nearest 1,000'.)

4. If you know there are about 5,000' in one mile, about how many miles would the difference in Problem 3 represent?

How do you know?

You may use a number line to help answer these questions.

1. In Los Angeles, the morning temperature was 65°F. That afternoon, the temperature rose 26 degrees. About how hot was it in the afternoon?

   (1) About −20°F

   (2) About 40°F

   (3) About 80°F

   (4) About 90°F

   (5) About 100°F

2. In Anchorage, Alaska, it was 15°F in the afternoon. That night the temperature dropped 25 degrees. How cold was it that night?

   (1) −25°F

   (2) −15°F

   (3) −10°F

   (4) −5°F

   (5) 25°F

3. Jana customizes vans. She estimated that a recent small job would cost $900. She spent $500 on equipment for the van and another $500 on labor. In the end, her books showed that for that job, she

   (1) Made $100.

   (2) Made $400.

   (3) Lost $100.

   (4) Lost $400.

   (5) Made $1,000.

4. Eric had trouble managing his checking account. His checkbook showed $575 in deposits and $750 in withdrawals. If Eric's starting balance was $0, what amount should you see in his checkbook register after these deposits and withdrawals?

   (1) −$225

   (2) −$175

   (3) −$150

   (4) −$125

   (5) $1,350

5. Use the following chart to answer the question: What is the difference between the highest and lowest temperature listed?

   Chart Of Plant Hardiness

Zone	Range of Average Annual *Minimum* Temperatures
Zone 3	−40° to −30°F
Zone 4	−30° to −20°F
Zone 5	−20° to −10°F
Zone 6	−10° to 0°F
Zone 7	0° to 10°F
Zone 8	10° to 20°F

   (1) −40°F

   (2) −30°F

   (3) 40°F

   (4) 50°F

   (5) 60°F

6. Find the difference between the highest recorded temperature in North America, 134°F, and the lowest recorded temperature in North America, −87°F.

Take Your Winnings

What is the largest amount you have ever won?

Some numbers are easier to work with than others. When you are doing mental math, some of the most friendly numbers are 10, 100, and 1,000.

In this lesson, you will think about the make-up of large amounts of money. How many $10, $100, or $1,000 bills are there in the same amount of money?

Noticing the make-up of large numbers can help you save time when you are adding or subtracting. Before you know it, you will be a human calculator!

Activity 1: How Do You Take Your Winnings?

Three friends pooled their money to buy a ticket for the Big Bucks lottery. They were astounded when they won the grand prize. After taxes, each friend received a voucher for $3,843. Each wanted to take her winnings in a different way:

Andrea wanted as much of her share in $1,000 bills as she could have. She thought big bills would be impressive!

Barbara didn't want $1,000 bills. She wanted her share in $100 bills because $100 bills would be easier to spend.

Carla wanted her money in $10 bills. She wanted lots of bills because she thought they would look like more money.

1. How did each person receive her money?

   Andrea:

   Barbara:

   Carla:

2. Suppose they won $2,105 each. How would each receive her money?

   Andrea:

   Barbara:

   Carla:

3. Suppose they won $11,035 each. How would each receive her money?

   Andrea:

   Barbara:

   Carla:

Activity 2: Concentration

You and a partner will receive 12 cards. Without looking at them, arrange the 12 cards face down on the table, in a 3-by-4 pattern.

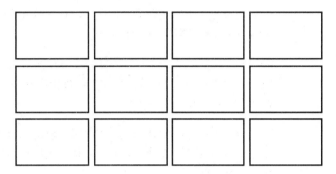

The object of the game is to win the most money.

Decide who will go first. The first player turns over two cards. If the cards match (show the same amount of money), the first player keeps the cards and takes another turn. If the cards do not match, he or she replaces them face down. Then the second player takes a turn. Continue until all the cards are matched.

The person with the most money wins.

After you have finished, together with your partner use the cards to write six equations for the matching pairs.

Activity 3: Mystery Numbers

You will need a calculator for this activity.

For each problem, follow these directions:

- Clear the calculator screen.

- Enter the starting number into your calculator.

- Decide what you need to do to arrive at the end number, and use the calculator to perform that operation.

- When you have found the correct operation and amount, write them in the middle column on the chart.

The first problem has been done for you.

Starting Number	Operation and Amount		End Number
1. 1,543	+ 30	=	1,573
2. 826		=	526
3. 1,988		=	3,988
4. 1,988		=	2,088
5. 7,070		=	7,670
6. 2,006		=	2,506
7. 4,260		=	4,240
8. 10,765		=	8,765
9. 9,999		=	9,599
10. 1,750		=	2,350

Practice: True or False?

Mark each statement T (true) or F (false). Rewrite all the false statements to make them true.

Statement	T or F?	False Statement Rewritten to Be True
1. 4 thousands = 40 hundreds		
2. 100(10) = 10(100)		
3. 6,503 = 6(1,000) + 53(10)		
4. 666 + 40 = 1,066		
5. 5,958 − 300 = 2,958		
6. 92(10) = 9(100) + 2(1)		
7. 57(100) + 4 = 5,704		
8. 2(1,000) + 5(100) = 20(100) + 50(10)		
9. 5(1,000) + 6(100) + 78(10) = 5,678		

Practice: More Mystery Numbers

You will need a calculator for this activity. For each problem:

- Clear the calculator screen.

- Enter the starting number into your calculator.

- Decide what you need to do to arrive at the end number, and use the calculator to perform that operation.

- When you have found the correct operation and amount, write them in the middle column on the chart.

The first one has been done for you.

Starting Number	Operation and Amount	End Number
1. 543	+ 1,000 =	1,543
2. 876	=	526
3. 1,088	=	3,088
4. 1,077	=	707
5. 21,156	=	25,156
6. 2,006	=	1,706
7. 4,640	=	4,590
8. 10,065	=	10,060
9. 9,009	=	9
10. 1,750	=	2,350

Practice: Calculating with Money

First add the amounts of money in your head and write down your answer.

Then do the math on the calculator and write down what appears on the screen.

	Mental Calculation	Calculator Result

1. 30¢ and 70¢ =

2. $30 and 70¢ =

3. $3 and 7¢ =

4. $30 and 7¢ =

5. $300 and $7 =

6. $8 and 9¢ =

7. $80 and 90¢ =

8. $8 and 90¢ =

9. 8¢ and 90¢ =

10. $80 and $90 =

11. Which is faster: mental math or the calculator? Why?

12. What do you notice about how the calculator shows money amounts?

Practice: College Registration

Kingsford College Fee Schedule

Single Credit:	$100.00
Course Credit:	3 credits each
Lab Credit:	Varies according to class, 1–3 credits each
Fees:	$3,900 (Includes technology fees, materials, and facilities fees)

Course Sampling

Arabic:	3 credits
Art—Figure Drawing:	3 credits
Astronomy for Beginners:	3 credits, plus 1 lab credit
Chemistry I:	3 credits, plus 3 lab credits
Civil Engineering:	3 credits, plus 2 lab credits
Creative Writing:	3 credits
Intro to Biology:	3 credits, plus 1 lab credit
Intro to Calculus:	3 credits
Landscape Design:	3 credits, plus 1 lab credit
Math for Nonmajors:	3 credits
Technical Writing:	3 credits
U.S. History—1800 to 1900:	3 credits

1. You just received a $5,000 scholarship to Kingsford College. What courses could you take and still have enough money to pay your fees charge?

2. How did you figure out the cost of your course load? Write an equation that shows the math you did.

Mental Math Practice: Double Trouble

Try to do as many of these doubling and halving problems as you can in your head. Use a calculator to check your answers.

1. This year was a wet year all over the United States. Average rainfall doubled in each region. What are the missing numbers?

Region	Average (inches)	This Year's Total (inches)
a. Midwest	_____	48
b. Southeast	_____	38
c. Northeast	44	_____
d. Northwest	_____	118
e. Southwest	9	_____

   f. What is true about the 1's digit in numbers that, when doubled, end in "8"? Will this be true in every case?

2. The coach of the wrestling team wants his team to work hard on strength training. He told the boys to aim to double the weight they can now lift.

Boy's Name	Current Weight	Goal
a. Bob	87 lbs.	_____
b. Martin	97 lbs.	_____
c. Horatio	107 lbs.	_____
d. Danny	117 lbs.	_____
e. Tony	127 lbs.	_____

   f. What is true about the 1's digit in all the answers?

3. The AIDS Ride trainer told me that I could easily bike double my weekly miles workout. (Circle the correct answer for each question.)

   a. How many miles would 16 miles doubled be?

   26   32   35   48   42

   b. How many miles would 36 miles doubled be?

   69   70   72   74   82

   c. How many miles would 56 miles doubled be?

   98   100   102   104   112

   d. What is the pattern? What is true for the answers 16, 36, and 56?

   e. If the AIDS Ride trainer is right, I can look at my goal and work backward to get my weekly training mileage.

Ride Goal	**Weekly Training Mileage**
(1) 92 miles	
(2) 96 miles	
(3) 108 miles	

1. John earned $5,906 last month. Which one of the following is *not* a way he could take his earnings?

    (1) 5($1,000) + 9($100) + 6($10)

    (2) 5($1,000) + 9($100) + 6($1)

    (3) 59($100) + 6($1)

    (4) 590($10) + 6($1)

    (5) 5($1,000) + 90($10) + 6($1)

2. 3($1,000) + 5($10) + 2($1) + 1($100) =

    (1) $1,135

    (2) $3,152

    (3) $3,521

    (4) $5,213

    (5) $5,352

3. Kay wants her youth group to raise more money this year than they ever have before. Last year's sales were $350; this year Kay wants to raise $900. How does this year's goal compare with last year's?

    (1) Ten times more than last year

    (2) About double last year's sales

    (3) About $600 more than last year

    (4) About ten times less than last year

    (5) About $6,000 more than last year

4. Vera's company has given her a sales goal of $5,000. She has sold $495 worth of merchandise. How does this amount compare with her goal?

    (1) Double what she has sold

    (2) About $500 less than what she has sold

    (3) About $5,000 more than what she has sold

    (4) About $500 more than what she has sold

    (5) About 10 times more than what she has sold

5. N stands for an unknown number. $N + 10 = 260$. What does N equal?

    (1) 26

    (2) 160

    (3) 250

    (4) 260

    (5) 270

6. How much more than 39,705 is 40,005?

7

LESSON

Patterns and Order

Which is faster— mental math or calculator?

People who are good at math notice and make good use of patterns. Keep that in mind as you look for as many patterns as you can in this lesson's activities, and use those patterns to make the computations go faster. In this lesson, you will use your mental math skills to solve problems and then see whether you can find the answers more quickly than the calculator.

You will also learn about the **order of operations** when writing equations and finding the value of expressions.

Whenever you use the calculator, remember to estimate first. Without an estimate, you may not know whether you have pressed a wrong key!

Activity 1: Mental Math or Calculator?

With a partner, solve each of the following problems.

- One of you will solve the problem using a calculator.
- The other will solve it using mental math.
- Check the box that indicates which was faster, mental math or the calculator.

Answer	Mental Math	Calculator
1. 90 x 10 =		
2. 300 ÷ 10 =		
3. 850 ÷ 10 =		
4. 8,500 x 10 =		
5. 900 x 100 =		
6. 3,000 ÷ 100 =		
7. 7,900 ÷ 10 =		
8. 7,900 ÷100 =		
9. 90 x 1,000 =		
10. 79,000 ÷ 1,000 =		

11. One thing I know about multiplying a number by 10:

12. One thing I know about dividing a number by 10:

13. One thing I know about multiplying a number by 100:

14. One thing I know about dividing a number by 100:

15. One thing I know about multiplying a number by 1,000:

16. One thing I know about dividing a number by 1,000:

Activity 2: 3, 4, 5

Part 1

1. Use the numbers 3, 4, and 5 (in any order) and two operations, addition and multiplication, to write as many number sentences as you can.

2. Now check your math with the calculator and compare the answers with yours above. If any are different, write the new answer next to the first answer.

Part 2

3. Solve each of the following problems on the calculator.
   Note the order in which the calculator computed
   the answer.

	Calculator Answer	Order of Operations

a. $1 + 9 \times 5 =$

b. $3 \times 7 + 2 =$

c. $12 \times 2 + 6 =$

d. $8 + 3 \times 4 =$

e. $10 \times 10 + 16 =$

f. $13 + 7 \times 3 =$

4. Use **parentheses** to rewrite the problems above, which the
   calculator does not work from left to right, to communicate that
   the order of the operations should be from left to right.

5. a. Use a calculator to solve $36 - 24 \div 4$.

   b. Solve $(36 - 24) \div 4$.

   c. How do these problems compare with the ones you solved in
      Problem 3? How are they the same? How are they different?

Practice: Just Like the Calculator

- Complete each number sentence on your own.
- Check your answers with a calculator.
- Make up two problems of your own and solve them.

	Your Answer	**Calculator Answer**

1. $3 + 6 \times 5 =$

2. $7 \times 7 + 2 =$

3. $4 \times 12 + 2 =$

4. $18 - 3 \times 4 =$

5. $10 \times 10 + 10 =$

6. $15 - 7 \times 2 =$

7.

8.

EMPower™

Practice: More or Less?

Estimate whether the answer is more or less than the amount given and circle your answer.

Show how you made your estimate. If you want, check your estimate using your calculator.

1. 54 x 4 is   more than 200   less than 200

How I made my estimate:

2. 370 x 2 is   more than 800   less than 800

How I made my estimate:

3. 203 x 5 is   more than 1,000   less than 1,000

How I made my estimate:

4. 89 x 3 is   more than 270   less than 270

How I made my estimate:

Mental Math Practice: Multiply and Divide with 10, 100, or 1,000

Do the calculations in your head and write down the answers.

Then check with a calculator.

Multiply fast!

1. 25 x 10 =

25 x 100 =

25 x 1,000 =

2. 205 x 10 =

205 x 100 =

205 x 1,000 =

3. 30 x 10 =

30 x 100 =

30 x 1,000 =

4. 360 x 10 =

360 x 100

360 x 1,000

Divide fast!

5. 6,000 ÷ 10 =

6,000 ÷ 100 =

6,000 ÷ 1,000 =

6. 100,000 ÷ 10 =

100,000 ÷ 100 =

100,000 ÷ 1,000 =

7. 36,000 ÷ 10 =

36,000 ÷ 100 =

36,000 ÷ 1,000 =

8. 306,000 ÷ 10 =

306,000 ÷ 100 =

306,000 ÷ 1,000 =

Extension: The Answer Is 24

1. Use two different operations (either addition and multiplication or division and subtraction) to write number sentences (equations) that equal 24. Use your calculator to check your equations.

   a.

   b.

   c.

   d.

2. Write a word problem that can be solved one of the following ways. The answer to your word problem must be 24.

   Circle the way you choose.

   a. By first multiplying and then adding

   b. By first adding and then dividing

   c. By first adding and then multiplying

   d. By first subtracting and then dividing

   My word problem:

   Solve your word problem. Use equations and pictures to show how you found your answer.

3. Write a different problem with the answer 24. Choose a different method than you did for Problem 2.

Circle the way you choose.

a. By first multiplying and then adding

b. By first adding and then dividing

c. By first adding and then multiplying

d. By first subtracting and then dividing

My word problem:

Solve your word problem. Use equations and pictures to show how you found your answer.

Extension: Wrong Number!

1. Veronica bought 10 postcards. Each one cost 40¢.

   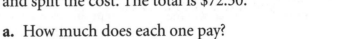

   a. How much did Veronica have to pay?

   b. The cashier rang up the total and got $400.00. Veronica gasped, "That can't be right!" Help the cashier—what went wrong?

2. Ten friends decide to have a picnic. They buy food and split the cost. The total is $72.50.

   a. How much does each one pay?

   b. Anton uses his calculator to find the answer. The display shows "62.5." Help Anton out—what went wrong?

3. Jorge buys 10 T-shirts on sale for $4.99 each.

   a. How much do the ten T-shirts cost?

   b. Jorge uses his calculator to find the answer. The display shows "14.99." He thinks he entered the correct numbers but the wrong operation. Help Jorge out—what went wrong?

1. Ten friends go to a bar. Their total cost, including tip, comes to $180. If each one pays the same amount, how much do they each contribute?

   (1) $10

   (2) $18

   (3) $28

   (4) $180

   (5) $190

2. Nick has $250 in savings. He needs 10 times that amount to buy a computer. How much will the computer cost?

   (1) $25

   (2) $250

   (3) $2,500

   (4) $25,000

   (5) $250,000

3. Nora sold a dozen roses in each of the 1,000 sales she made since opening her flower business six months ago. All together, how many roses did Nora sell?

   (1) 120 roses

   (2) 240 roses

   (3) 1,000 roses

   (4) 1,200 roses

   (5) 12,000 roses

4. Diego traveled four hours at 50 mph, stopped for lunch, then traveled three more hours at 60 mph. The expression that will help us find how many miles Diego traveled is:

   (1) $(3 \times 50) + (4 \times 60)$

   (2) $(3 + 4) \times 55$

   (3) $3 + 4 \times 50 + 60$

   (4) $(4 \times 50) + (3 \times 60)$

   (5) $(4 + 50) \times (3 + 60)$

5. If the solution is 120, which of the following problems was solved?

   (1) $35 - 5 \times 4$

   (2) $(35 - 5) \times 4$

   (3) $(60 - 20) \div 3$

   (4) $60 - 20 \times 3$

   (5) $(150 - 2) \times 15$

6. $(680 + 320) \div 100 = ?$

Picture This

> *How many are there?*
> *How do you know?*

Counting is important in our everyday lives. Knowing how to total the items in a group efficiently is valuable because it saves time.

In this lesson, you will look at familiar objects arranged in groups, and you will be asked to find the total without counting each object. You will also write mathematical expressions that show that total.

For instance, if there are two six-packs of soda, you might write this:

6 + 6   6(2)   *or*   2(6)

These are **equivalent expressions**; their total, 12, is the same.

Activity 1: Pictures and Numbers

Part 1

Choose one picture from this page and one from the next page. For each, find the total number of objects in the picture, but don't count one by one. Write down two or more ways to find the total.

1. Soda Cans

2. Fingers

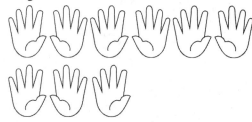

3. Heads

Reprinted with permission of *World Education*

4. Stamps

5. Chocolates

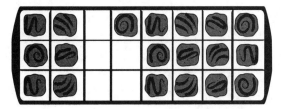

Part 2

Each of the following expressions describes one of the arrays drawn below. Find the expression that best matches each **array** and write its letter on the line provided.

    a. 10 x 13 + 1 x 13

    b. 11(10) + 11(3)

    c. 10(10) + 10(1) + 3(10) + 3(1)

    d. 10 x 10 + 1 x 13 + 3 x 10

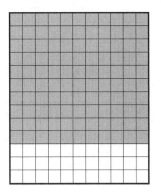

1. Expression: _____

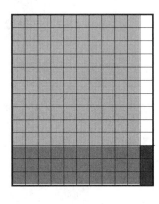

3. Expression: _____

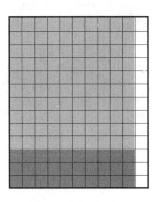

2. Expression: _____

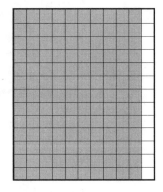

4. Expression: _____

5. a. 11 × 13 = _____

   b. How did you find the answer?

If you used yet another array to help you find the answer, sketch it below.

6. Explain why the expressions in Problem 1 are equivalent expressions.

Activity 2: Counting Smart

Part 1

Take a handful of paper clips, pennies, or tiles. Arrange them as arrays so you can see how many there are without counting each one.

1. Sketch your arrangement using columns and rows.

2. Write an equation that shows how you can find the total amount without counting each item.

3. Sketch another arrangement. If you did not try arranging by 10's, try that now.

4. Write an expression that shows how you found the total amount without counting each item.

Part 2

Draw a picture that communicates each mathematical expression.

    1. $4 \times 9 + 2$

    2. $20 - 3 \times 5$

    3. $3 \times 4 \times 5$

    4. $3(4 + 6)$

    5. Now pick one of the mathematical expressions above and write a word problem for it.

Activity 3: Garden Pathway

Valerie and Rebecca own a landscaping business. A customer wants them to install a garden and a square-tile pathway surrounding it. This is the picture the customer provided.

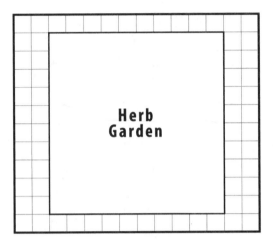

Each woman saw the math differently. Of course, they didn't count each tile! Show two different ways that Valerie and Rebecca could have figured out the number of tiles.

1. First way:

2. Second way:

Practice: Cartons of Eggs

1. Without counting each egg, how many do you see?

2. How did you think of your answer?

3. List with words and numbers each step you took mentally or on paper to find the total.

4. Write another expression to show how you could count the eggs.

Practice: Expressions, Arrays, and Stories

Part 1

Below you will see three partially or totally filled arrays. Each is preceded by several expressions. Circle the expressions that do *not* match what you see.

> *Reminder*: Parentheses indicate multiplication or tell you to do the operation inside them first.

1. 10 + 10 + 3   3 x 3 + 10   10 x 2 + 3   3 + 2(10)

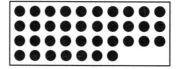

2. 3 x 10 + 7   10 + 10 + 10 + 7   3(10 + 3)   4 x 7 − 3

3. 5 + 5 + 5 + 5 + 5   5(5)   5 x 5 + 5 + 5 + 5 5^2

Part 2

Choose one of the arrays above to match each story.

4. Zippy and four friends pool their money. Each person contributes five dollars.   Array _____

5. Zippy and two friends decide to go in together on a gift for their teacher. Zippy's two friends have 10 dollars each to give. Zippy has only three dollars.   Array _____

6. Three friends and Zippy decide to share the cost of a take-out order from the local restaurant. Everybody gives 10 dollars but Zippy. He is three dollars short.   Array _____

Practice: How Do You See It?

Find how many things are in each picture without actually counting each one. Use equations or explain in words your way of finding the total.

Is there a way to find the total by just adding two numbers? How about by adding three numbers?

Is there a way to find the total in each picture by multiplying and adding?

1. Circle the groups you see in each picture as you figure out the total. Write an expression that describes what you see.

   a.

   Expression: _____

   b.

   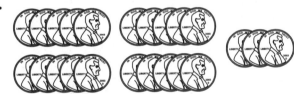

   Expression: _____

   c.

   Expression: _____

2. Show how you find the total number of tiles. Is there more than one way?

Practice: Stone Paths

The following are rectangular arrays for paths made using 12 flat stones.

1. For each one, write a multiplication expression that describes the array.

    a.

    Equation:_____

    b.

    Equation:_____

    c.

    Equation:_____

2. **a.** Find all the possible stone path arrays for 23, 24, and 25 stones. Use the grid paper on the next two pages to draw the arrays.

    b. Write equations that describe each of the arrays you find.

    c. Why are there more paths for 24 stones?

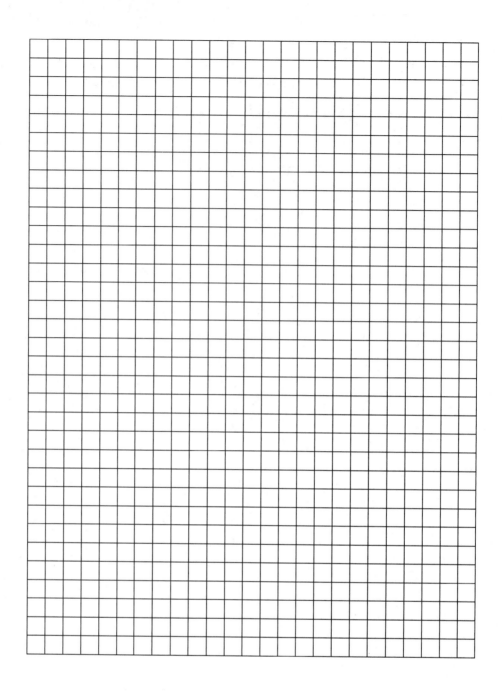

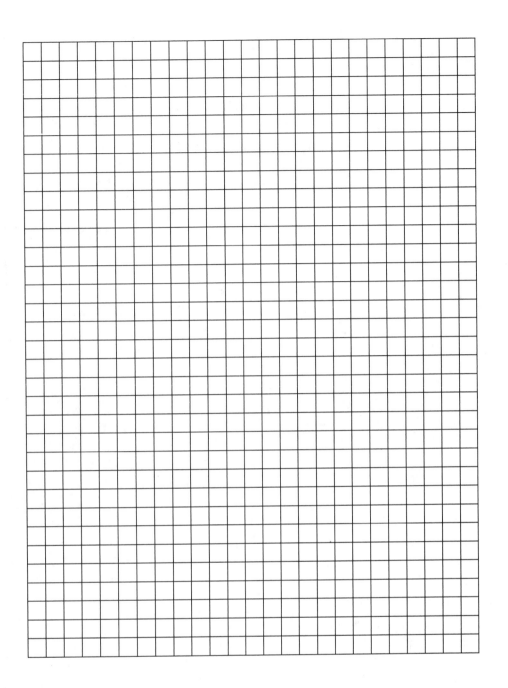

Mental Math Practice: Square Numbers

You **square** a number by multiplying it by itself. You can use an **exponent** (a small, raised number) to show the multiplication. For example, 5 x 5 can be written as 5^2. You read that as "five squared."

1. Square all the whole numbers from 0–12.

n	0	1	2	3	4	5	6
n^2							

n	7	8	9	10	11	12
n^2						

2. Fill the missing numbers in the boxes to make each equation true.

   a. $\boxed{}$ x $\boxed{}$ = 36

   b. $\boxed{}$ x 9 =

   c. $9 = \boxed{}^2$

   d. $8^2 = \boxed{}$

   e. $0^2 + 1^2 + 2^2 + 3^2 = \boxed{}$

How many rolls of film are missing in the black area? How do you know?

Extension: Seeing Squarely

Square numbers can look like square-shaped arrangements. Draw an arrangement of objects for these equations:

1. 5^2

2. $5^2 + 3^2$

3. $(5 + 3)^2$

4. $5^2 - 3^2$

1. Which of the following arrays matches the equation 3 x 4 = 12?

   A.

   B.

   C.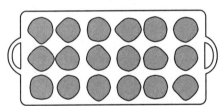

   (1) A

   (2) B

   (3) C

   (4) A and B

   (5) B and C

2. Which of the following expressions might be used to count the cookies on the tray?

   A. 6+ 6+ 6   B. 6 x 3   C. 6 x 6

   (1) A only

   (2) B only

   (3) C only

   (4) A and B

   (5) A and C

3. Frankie needs 45 tiles to cover the bathroom floor in her apartment. The picture below shows how many she has already installed. Which of these expressions shows the number of tiles Frankie still needs to install to finish the job?

   (1) 4 x 9

   (2) 45 + 4(9)

   (3) 4(9) x 45

   (4) 45 – (4 x 9)

   (5) (45 – 4) x 9

4. Select the expression that is *not* equivalent to the rest of the expressions.

   (1) 3 x 4 x 2

   (2) 3(4 x 2)

   (3) (4 + 4 + 4) x 2

   (4) (3 + 3 + 3 + 3) x 2

   (5) 3(4 + 2)

5. Charlie's Windows charges $6 a window for cleaning. Which of the following expressions shows how much Charlie's Windows will charge the customer?

(1) 6(3 ✕ 4)

(2) 6 + (3 ✕ 4)8

(3) 8(12 + 6)

(4) 6(4 x 12)

(5) 6(3 ✕ 4 ✕ 8)

6. Lois enters a party room and sees round tables. Eight people are seated at each of 12 tables and five people at two other tables. How many people does Lois see?

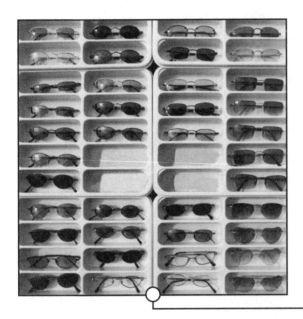

What's the Story?

What math do you see in this picture?

Solving a problem starts with understanding it: What is the story? What is happening? Get a picture in your mind. Once you have figured that out and have drawn the picture or written a mathematical equation for it, you are ready to solve the problem.

In the previous lesson, you made connections between mathematical expressions and pictures. Keep that in mind as you add another element—word problems. The focus of the lesson is on word (or story) problems that can be solved in different ways. You will use pictures and equations to show your solutions.

Activity 1: What's the Story?

Problem 1

Laura is employed washing windows. Her current job involves washing windows on three-story buildings. There are *four* of these buildings and each one has the same front window arrangement:

First floor—12 windows

Second floor—12 windows

Third floor—10 windows

How many front windows will she wash for this job?

Person A

Person A started by thinking about how many windows were in one building. Continue his thinking.

1. What is the picture? Draw it.

2. What mathematics do you see in the picture? Write some equations.

3. What is the answer? Explain how Person A solved the problem.

Person B

Person B began by thinking about how many first-floor windows there were altogether. Continue her thinking.

1. What is the picture? Draw it.

2. What mathematics do you see in the picture? Write some equations.

3. What is the answer? Explain how Person B solved the problem.

Problem 2

Discount T-shirts come in packs of three. Lana needs to get a T-shirt for each child in the preschool where she works. There are four classes of nine children each. How many packs does she need?

Person A

Person A started by thinking about how many children there were altogether. Continue her thinking.

1. What is the picture? Draw it.

2. What mathematics do you see in the picture? Write some equations.

3. What is the answer? Explain how Person A solved the problem.

Person B

Person B started out by thinking about how many packs of T-shirts one class would need. Continue his thinking.

1. What is the picture? Draw it.

2. What mathematics do you see in the picture? Write some equations.

3. What is the answer? Explain how Person B solved the problem.

Activity 2: The Rose Problem

Erin bought some roses to resell. She paid $6.00 for every 12 roses she bought. Later, Erin was charging $6.00 for eight roses. She sold them all and made a profit of $12.00. How many roses did Erin buy and resell?

Practice: Drawings and Equations

For each of the following problems, draw the arrangement of objects, write equations, and then solve the problem.

1. "Someone has been taking soda from our inventory," Garret announced. "We had 10 six-packs to start. Now there are two cans missing from each of five of those six-packs and four cans missing from each of the other five. This means there are only ____ cans left."

2. Holiday paper cups come in packs of eight. Alberto expects a total of 16 people at his party. He needs three cups per person. How many packages will he need to buy?

3. A case of hot sauce costs $9.00. Hot sauce comes five bottles to a case. Tia has to order 30 bottles of hot sauce for her restaurant. How much will she spend on hot sauce for her restaurant?

4. Linus buys used CD's at three for $8, and sells them at three for $20. If he sells 30 CD's, how much profit does he make?

Practice: Equations and Word Problems

Look at each arrangement of objects. First write an equation for the math you see in the picture. Then write a word problem that could match the arrangement.

1.

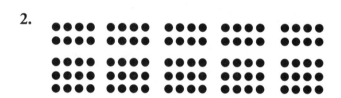

2.

3.

Practice: The Answer Is _____

You will be writing a word problem.

1. Circle the number that will be the answer to your word problem.

    15   20   36   42   60   72

2. Write a word problem that can be solved by *multiplying*. The answer will be the number you circled.

    My word problem:

    Solve your word problem. Use equations and pictures to show how you found your answer.

3. Write another problem with the same answer. This time, write a word problem that could be solved by *multiplying and adding* or by *multiplying and subtracting*.

    My word problem:

    Solve your word problem. Use equations and pictures to show how you found your answer.

Everyone has had a problem in his or her life that involved math. Can you think of a time when you did? Whether it involved paying bills, buying something on time, making something, or figuring out how much of something you needed, the situation caused you to think about numbers.

Describe a time when you had to solve a problem in your head that involved numbers. Be sure to tell *all* the steps you ended up doing to solve the problem.

One Day, I...

Equations I Used

Show step-by-step how you solved your problem.

Mental Math Practice: Patterns in the Multiplication Table

There are so many patterns in the multiplication table. For example, all the multiples of 10 end in zero. What other patterns do you see?

x	0	1	2	3	4	5	6	7	8	9	10	11	12
0	0	0	0	0	0	0	0	0	0	0	0	0	0
1	0	1	2	3	4	5	6	7	8	9	10	11	12
2	0	2	4	6	8	10	12	14	16	18	20	22	24
3	0	3	6	9	12	15	18	21	24	27	30	33	36
4	0	4	8	12	16	20	24	28	32	36	40	44	48
5	0	5	10	15	20	25	30	35	40	45	50	55	60
6	0	6	12	18	24	30	36	42	48	54	60	66	72
7	0	7	14	21	28	35	42	49	56	63	70	77	84
8	0	8	16	24	32	40	48	56	64	72	80	88	96
9	0	9	18	27	36	45	54	63	72	81	90	99	108
10	0	10	20	30	40	50	60	70	80	90	100	110	120
11	0	11	22	33	44	55	66	77	88	99	110	121	132
12	0	12	24	36	48	60	72	84	96	108	120	132	144

The patterns I see:

1. Tom said he figured out the number of tiles needed for the floor of his laundry space with the equation 8 x 4+ 2. Which of the following arrangements shows a possible tile arrangement for Tom's laundry floor?

A.    B.

C. 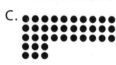   D.

E.

   (1) A

   (2) B

   (3) C

   (4) D

   (5) E

2. Every month, Marlene pays $16 for basic local phone service. Most months she has no extra charge. This past year, she did have an extra charge of $10 for one month. Which of the following expressions shows a way to find how much Marlene paid for her phone service this past year?

   (1) 12($10) + $16

   (2) 12($16) + $10

   (3) 12($16 + $10)

   (4) $16(12 + $10)

   (5) $16($10) + 12

3. Eric charged 10 items last month on his credit card. Each item cost about $25. When he received his bill, he noticed that he had a $25 credit from a returned purchase made the previous month. What is the amount of Eric's current bill?

   (1) $60

   (2) $175

   (3) $225

   (4) $250

   (5) $275

4. Sara works at a daycare center. Each day she usually uses four six-packs of juice for the toddlers and one package of crackers. Each toddler gets one serving of juice. Today, three toddlers are absent. Which of the following expressions shows the number of juices Sara will use today?

   (1) 4 x 6

   (2) 4(6) + 3

   (3) 4(6) − 3

   (4) 24 ÷ 6

   (5) 24 ÷ 4

5. Which of the following is a good picture for $5^2 - 3$?

A. B. C.

D. E.

(1) A

(2) B

(3) C

(4) D

(5) E

6. $10(4 + 5) =$

Deal Me In

How much will it cost per month?

Using mental math strategies can help you make smart and quick decisions. Savvy consumers often multiply and divide mentally to predict costs for a year or to break down costs to a per month amount. For example: The monthly electric bill is $32.00—what will that cost for a year? The yearly car insurance payment is $800—what will monthly installments cost? Sometimes you want to compare two choices to see which is better; sometimes you just want to know whether you can afford an item.

In this lesson, you answer the question: "What will the monthly payment be if I buy on time?" You will discuss strategies for answering the question. To use mental math for these division problems, you may break a problem into simpler parts to find the solution.

Activity 1: Easy Payments

Expensive items are often paid off over several months. First, estimate the monthly payment for each plan.

Next, figure out in your head exactly how much you would pay each month if you spread out the payments.

Finally, record your method for how you thought it out.

Payment Plan	Estimated Monthly Payment	Exact Monthly Payment
1. $9,600 over 4 months		
2. $9,600 over 8 months		
3. $9,600 over 12 months		
4. $9,600 over 24 months		

5. My method for figuring out Payment Plan 1:

6. My method for figuring out Payment Plan 2:

7. My method for figuring out Payment Plan 3:

8. My method for figuring out Payment Plan 4:

9. Now check your math with the calculator. Do all your results agree?

Activity 2: The Payment Plan Game

Your team will get a total when it is your turn. You need to figure out the payment.

Put your heads together to come up with the best answer you can. No pencils and paper or calculators! This is mental math teamwork.

Be prepared to explain your reasoning process for coming up with the answer.

The other teams either *challenge* if they think they can give a better answer than yours or *pass* if they think the answer is a good one. Challenging teams must explain their reasoning as well.

Scoring System

+5 points for a good team estimate with reasoning

+10 points for an even closer challenge with reasoning

−5 points for a wrong estimate (way off)

−5 points for an incorrect challenge (not as close as the answer given by the team whose turn it is)

−5 for not challenging a wrong estimate

The team with the most points at the end wins. Good luck!

Keep track of your team's score here:

Practice: Four Ways to Write Division

Division can be written in several ways.

If this is a picture of one candy bar...

This would mean 10 candy bars divided between 2 people.

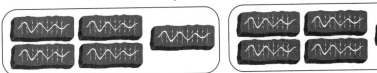

| $2)\overline{10}$ | $10 \div 2$ | $\dfrac{10}{2}$ | 10 divided by 2 |

Be careful: The order of the numbers makes a difference in division.

This would mean 2 candy bars divided among 10 people.

| $10)\overline{2}$ | $2 \div 10$ | $\dfrac{2}{10}$ | 2 divided by 10 |

Complete each row by writing the division three other ways.

$8)\overline{56}$	$56 \div 8$	$\dfrac{56}{8}$	56 divided by 8
	$30 \div 5$		
$6)\overline{180}$			
	$40 \div 1$		
			2 divided by 7
		$\dfrac{x}{y}$	
			m divided by 10
$\$0.50)\overline{\$10.00}$			

Practice: Which Is Not the Same?

Order makes a difference in division: $10 \div 5$ is not the same as $5 \div 10$!

Use what you know about division notation and rules of order to choose the one expression that is *not* the same as the others.

1. **a.** $28 \div 7$

    b. 28 divided by 7

    c. $28\overline{)7}$

    d. $\dfrac{28}{7}$

2. **a.** $\dfrac{15}{1,000}$

    b. $1,000 \div 15$

    c. $15\overline{)1,000}$

    d. $\dfrac{1,000}{15}$

3. **a.** 10 divided by 60

    b. $(64 - 4) \div 10$

    c. $10\overline{)60}$

    d. $\dfrac{60}{10}$

4. **a.** $(100 + 80) \div 4$

    b. $100 + (80 \div 4)$

    c. $(100 \div 4) + 20$

    d. $25 + 20$

Practice: Those Monthly Payments

In the following problems, is the monthly payment for the first amount given greater than (>), less than (<), or equal to (=) the monthly payment for the second amount? Assume all payments are evenly split. Do the math in your head.

Example:

$1,800 over 3 months   > $2,000 over 4 months

1. $1,500 over 5 months   _____ $1,200 over 3 months

2. $1,000 over 4 months   _____ $600 over 3 months

3. $2,000 over 5 months   _____ $1,800 over 4 months

4. $500 over 3 months   _____ $700 over 4 months

Practice: 10's, 100's, and 1,000's

Breaking apart numbers to solve multiplication or division problems makes you think about how numbers are put together. Here are five problems for practice.

Start to solve each problem as indicated. Then complete it. Show your work.

1. $12 \times 9 =$

   Start with $10 \times 9 =$

   Then:

2. 21×11

   Start with $21 \times 10 =$

   Then:

3. 25×23

   Start with 25×10

   Then:

4. $130 \div 5$

   Start with $100 \div 5 =$

   Then:

5. $1,272 \div 4$

   Start with $1,000 \div 4$

   Then:

Mental Math Practice: Flowers by the Month

Solve these problems without using a pencil and paper.

> Remember: Work with 10's and 1's. Look for patterns with zeroes.

For one problem, explain how you found your answers using mental math.

1.

**Flowers at
Your Door**

Join the Flower Club!

Pay Monthly:

12 months: $ _____

10 months: $ 160.00

6 months: $ _____

2 months: $ 32.00

Monthly: $ _____

2.

Roses Galore

Monthly Flower Club

Payments:

12 months: $ _____

10 months: $ 380.00

6 months: $ _____

2 months: $ 76.00

Monthly: $ _____

3.

**Foster's
Flowers**

Flower Club of the Month

Pay by the Month:

12 months: $ _____

10 months: $ 270.00

6 months: $ _____

2 months: $ 54.00

Monthly: $ _____

1. Thirty people were waiting to check out. If the three check-out lines were equal, how many people were in each line? Which of the following expressions matches the story?

    (1) 3 divided by 30

    (2) 30 divided by 3

    (3) $\frac{3}{30}$

    (4) 3 x 30

    (5) $\frac{10}{30}$

2. The car insurance payment is $789.50 a year. If Jo pays it quarterly, that means she pays about how much each time?

    (1) Less than $10

    (2) Less than $100

    (3) About $150

    (4) About $200

    (5) About $400

3. How much will 11 lines of advertising cost for one day?

    ### *World Times Report*
    #### CLASSIFIED

    Call to place your ad today!

    #### Help Wanted Weekday Special
    #### $2.90 per line per day

    Requirements:
    • Same ad to run 3 times in 6 days
    • Monday thru Saturday
    • Maximum size: 150 lines
    • Minimum size: 7 lines

    (1) $29.00

    (2) $31.90

    (3) $32.90

    (4) $2,900

    (5) $2,990

4. George works 40 hours a week, and his gross weekly salary is $680 per week. How much does George earn per hour?

    (1) $7

    (2) $7.50

    (3) $12

    (4) $15

    (5) $17

5. Use the information in Problem 4 to decide how much George's gross monthly salary should be.

    (1) Less than $2,000

    (2) Between $2,000 and $2,500

    (3) Between $2,700 and $3,400

    (4) Between $3,500 and $4,000

    (5) More than $4,000

6. How much will the Grand Cherokee cost for a one-year lease?

    ### Every 2005 Jeep Grand Cherokee Limited 4x4

    ## $399 per month

    • Available Quadra-Drive II® 4WD
    • Available 5.7-liter HEMI® V8 w/MDS
    • Leather-trimmed seating
    • Boston Acoustics premium sound system
    • AM/FM stereo six-disc CD/MP3 player

String It Along

> *How will this woman use division?*

In the last lesson, you looked at the operation of division as a way to split up an amount into equal parts. You interpreted 52 ÷ 4 as 52 objects split into four piles and $9,600 ÷ 10 as $9,600 split into 10 equal payments.

In this lesson, you will take a different look at division. When you see 52 ÷ 4, you will ask yourself, "How many fours are in 52?" As you work with measurements, keep in mind the ways the pictures of division and multiplication relate.

Activity 1: String It Along

Part 1

In Envelope A, there are four pieces of string.

Look at the three short pieces of string. They are 3″, 4″, and 6″ long.

1. How many of each of the short pieces of string fit into the longest string?

   a. There are _____ 3″ strings in the longest string.

   b. There are _____ 4″ strings in the longest string.

   c. There are _____ 6″ strings in the longest string.

2. How many inches long is the longest string? How do you know?

3. Make three sketches that show the relationship of each of the short strings to the longest string.

4. Write three equations that show the relationship of each of the short strings to the longest string.

Part 2

In Envelope B, there are four pieces of string.

Look at the three short pieces of string. They are 6″, 9″, and 18″ long.

1. How many of each of the short pieces of string fit into the longest string?

   a. There are _____ 6″ strings in the longest string.

   b. There are _____ 9″ strings in the longest string.

   c. There are _____ 18″ strings in the longest string.

2. How many inches long is the longest string? How do you know?

3. Make three sketches that show the relationship of each of the short strings to the longest string.

4. Write three equations that show the relationship of each of the short strings to the longest string.

Activity 2: Scales on Maps

Use what you know about map scales to figure out how many miles the distance is between the following cities.

1. **Map 1**: The scale is 1 inch to 710 miles.

    1 inch = 710 miles

Distance between Cities on Scaled Map	Distance in Actual Miles
a. Seattle, WA, to Santa Cruz, CA = 1 inch	
b. Miami, FL, to Seattle, WA = 4 inches	
c. Los Angeles, CA, to Toronto, Canada = 3 inches	

2. **Map 2**: The scale is 4 cm to 100 miles.

    4 cm = 100 miles

    0   1   2   3   4

Distance between Cities on Scaled Map	Distance in Actual Miles
a. Birmingham, AL, to Oakland, CA = 80 cm	
b. Miami, FL, to Chicago, IL = 48 cm	
c. Dallas, TX, to Los Angeles, CA = 12 cm	
d. Seattle, WA, to San Francisco, CA = 50 cm	

3. How far apart would you expect these cities to be on the scaled maps? How do you know?

Cities	Distance between Cities (in miles)	Map 1 Scaled Distance (in inches)	Map 2 Scaled Distance (in cm)
a. Chicago, IL, to Madison, WI	150		
b. Boston, MA, to Philadelphia, PA	300		
c. Chicago, IL, to Tokyo, Japan	7,500		

4. Compare the scale on Map 1 with that on Map 2. What is the same and what is different?

Practice: How Many Blanks in a Blank?

1. **a.** How many 12″ rulers are in a 36″ yardstick?

   b. Division equation:

   c. Picture or number line:

2. **a.** How many 15-minute periods are in a 60-minute game?

   b. Division equation:

   c. Picture or number line:

3. **a.** How many 16-oz. cups are in a 128-oz. (gallon) container?

   b. Division equation:

   c. Picture or number line:

4. **a.** How many tons (2,000 lbs.) of rocks are in a 10,000-lb. truckload?

   b. Division equation:

   c. Picture or number line:

5. a. How many accounting quarters (three months long) are in a two-year period?

b. Division equation:

c. Picture or number line:

6. a. Use your favorite coffee or teacup to fill up a bucket or soda bottle. There are about _____ teacups in a _____.

b. Division equation:

c. Picture or number line:

Practice: About How Many Times as Large?

Answer each of the following problems and show how you found an approximate answer.

1. LeAnn is seven years old. Her grandmother, Lupa, is 72. About how many times older than LeAnn is Lupa?

2. Sergio weighs 140 pounds. His daughter, Marissa, weighs 68 pounds. About how many times heavier than Marissa is Sergio?

3. Marcel weighs 197 pounds. His kitten weighs only 2 pounds. About how many times heavier than his kitten is Marcel?

4. Gino is 6 feet tall. His son, Derrick, is 35 inches tall. About how many times taller is Gino than Derrick?

Practice: Coin Rolling

1. **a.** How many pennies equal one dollar?

    b. How many nickels equal one dollar?

    c. How many dimes equal one dollar?

    d. How many quarters equal one dollar?

Each child in a family has $12 in change. Each one has saved a different coin denomination and wants to roll the coins. Do any of the children have some change left over after making as many complete rolls of coins as he or she can? Show how you know with pictures, words, and equations.

2. How many 50¢ penny rolls can the child with $12 in pennies make?

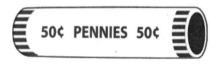

3. How many $2 nickel rolls can the child who saved $12 in nickels make?

4. How many $5 dime rolls can the child who saved $12 in dimes make?

5. How many $10 quarter rolls can the child who saved $12 in quarters make?

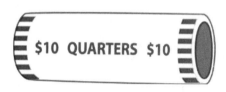

6. If you rolled change with *three* different types of coins, what is one possible way you could roll exactly $24? What is another way?

Practice: Vacation Spots

Every winter Grandpa and Grandma leave Chicago and drive somewhere warmer. Grandpa drives his car. Manuel and Lena help out by driving a van and their truck to the new place.

Circle a destination and total mileage or choose one of your own.

Key Largo, FL   Phoenix, AZ   Los Angeles, CA

1,500 miles   1,800 miles   2,000 miles

- Lena drives the van and averages 50 miles per hour.

- Manuel drives their truck at 75 miles per hour.

- Grandpa drives his car at 65 miles per hour.

1. How many hours did each person drive to reach the warmer city? Show your work in math symbols.

    a. Lena (van):

    b. Manuel (truck):

    c. Grandpa (car):

2. Choose Problem 1a, 1b, or 1c and draw a diagram, number line, or picture to demonstrate your answer for that problem.

Practice: Collecting Frequent Flyer Miles

Fly High Airlines is offering a free ticket to travelers who fly 25,000 miles.

1. Nina makes a business trip from Atlanta, Georgia, to Orlando, Florida. The one-way trip is 397 miles. How many round trips will she need to take to earn a free ticket?

   Show your work.

2. Jean Marie's mother is sick. Jean Marie flies as often as she can from Dallas to New Orleans. The one-way trip is 447 miles. How many round trips will she need to make to earn a free ticket?

   Show your work.

Mental Math Practice: Factors

Thinking about all the **factors** in a number can help you do multiplication and division more quickly.

The factors of any whole number are the whole numbers that can be divided into the number evenly.

Some numbers have many factors. Others have only two.

12 has six factors: 1, 2, 3, 4, 6, and 12.

13 has only two factors: 1 and 13.

1. List all the factors of the following numbers:

    a. 20

    b. 23

    c. 24

    d. 25

2. Fill in the blanks, using the numbers 20, 23, 24, and 25, to make each sentence a true statement.

    a. Five is a factor of _____ and _____.

    b. Twelve is a factor of _____.

    c. Ten is a factor of _____.

    d. The number with only two factors is _____.

    e. The number with the most factors is _____.

Envelopes can be bought from the Acme Envelope Company singly or in packages. Here is the Acme price list:

Plain White Business Envelopes
(4" x 9")
Single 5¢ each
10 pack box 39¢
100 pack box $2.59
1000 pack box $19.99

Specialty Invitation Envelopes
(4" x 7") *Available in 6 pastel colors*
Single 7¢ each
10 pack box 69¢
100 pack box $5.99
1000 pack box $38.99

Use the information in the price list to answer the following questions.

1. The office manager estimates that the staff uses 480 envelopes a year. Think about how many envelopes are used in one month. What expression could you use to solve this problem?

    (1) 480 x 12

    (2) $\frac{480}{12}$

    (3) 12 ÷ 480

    (4) $\frac{12}{480}$

    (5) 12 x 480

2. The purchasing officer of a small corporation decides to order 20,000 white envelopes for the coming year. She wants to order them in 1,000-pack boxes. How many boxes should she order?

    (1) 10

    (2) 20

    (3) 1,000

    (4) 2,000

    (5) 20,000

3. Tasha wants to buy 1,500 specialty envelopes for invitations for various community center functions in equal amounts of three pastel colors: yellow, green, and blue. How many 10-pack boxes should she buy of each color?

    (1) 15

    (2) 25

    (3) 50

    (4) 150

    (5) 500

4. After the mid-winter inventory was taken, the count of white business envelopes left in the stockroom was 12,587. Andre decided to repack them into 100-pack boxes. How many boxes will he use?

    (1) 12

    (2) 13

    (3) 125

    (4) 126

    (5) 1,258

5. Wilbur ordered 50 100-pack specialty envelopes in pastel blue. He returned 35 of the packs in exchange for a comparable number of 100-packs of pastel yellow. How many envelopes of each color were in his final order?

    (1) 35 yellow and 50 blue

    (2) 350 yellow and 500 blue

    (3) 350 yellow and 150 blue

    (4) 3,500 yellow and 1,500 blue

    (5) 1,500 yellow and 3,500 blue

6. Denise has driven between two cities and knows the distance is 135 miles. On the map she is using, the scale is 1 inch = 45 miles. How many inches apart will the two cities be on Denise's map?

Making Do

What do I do with the leftovers?

One of the challenges when solving a problem with division is deciding what to do about the remainder, if there is one.

In this lesson you make judgment calls about leftovers in division problems. A **remainder,** or the leftover amount in a problem, can be left as it is. Sometimes you may need to decide to round the answer up or down, or the remainder can be written and read as a fraction or a decimal. You decide: What makes the most sense?

Activity 1: Party Favors

Deanna's aunt planned a birthday party for her. She bought party favors for Deanna and the four children invited (five children in all). Suddenly the plans have changed. Another child is coming! Now there will be six children at the party. To be fair, all the children should get the same number of party favors. Look at the list of favors. How did Deanna's aunt divide up the goodies? Was she able to divide everything evenly or were there leftovers?

Mark each item in the blank provided:

E for Evenly Divided—no leftovers when divided six ways

SL for Split the Leftovers—parts of the items to each

CS for Can't Split the Leftovers—save them for later

Final List of Party Favors (Amount for Each of Six Children)

1. 30 stickers _____

2. 15 balloons _____

3. 60 marbles _____

4. 15 packs of Lifesavers™ (11 pieces of candy)_____

5. 15 packs of gum (6 sticks each) _____

6. 5 gift certificates for $1.00 each _____

7. 35 gummy bears _____

8. 15 quarters for the jukebox _____

9. 10 picture books _____

10. 25 sparklers _____

Activity 2: Making Do

A foreman usually sends out his work crews to three sites. Today he has to send them to four sites, but he only has supplies for three sites. Use the following list that shows how much material would have been sent to each of three sites to show how much of each item will now go to the crews at four work sites.

Note whether an item can be divided evenly or is likely to have some leftover amount.

On Hand: Supplies for Each of Three Sites	Making Do: Supplies for Four Sites
1. 15 feet of wire	
2. 240 feet of board	
3. 270 feet of rope	
4. 3 boxes of 70-count screws	
5. 3 cans of paint	
6. 30 pounds of plaster	
7. 6 40-pound bags of cement mix	
8. 2 pallets of stone (160 count each)	

Practice: Interpreting Remainders

Each situation has a matching answer. What does the answer mean? Is it a number of people, dollars, cards, or Lifesavers? Draw lines to connect the matching situations to their answers.

Situation

1. Six cups of milk for four children

2. Four office cubicles shared by eight people

3. 30 paragraphs read aloud by three people

4. 20 miles per gallon on a trip of 1,100 miles

5. 10 pages of space in a newsletter shared by four people

6. 30 pounds of plaster for 12 students

7. 100 CD's, six to a carrying case

8. Two pallets of stone (160 count each) for three walkways

9. 90° angle divided into two parts

10. 13 bricks in three rows

11. 11 hours into two parts

12. Seven skeins of yarn for two baby sweaters

Answers

a. 5.5

b. four and one left over

c. 45

d. one-half

e. 16 and 4 left over

f. 55

g. 3 and one half

h. 1 plus two fourths or $1\frac{1}{2}$

i. $2\frac{1}{2}$

j. 10

k. 106 r2

l. 2.5

Practice: Pill Problems

1. Monica takes one allergy pill in the morning and one at night. The pills come in a bottle of 150. How many days will the pills last?

2. Tracy takes two pills every four hours for three days. Then she takes two pills every six hours until they are used up. The pills come in bottles of 100. Will her pills last one month? Explain.

3. The doctor prescribed Malia three tablets every four hours for two weeks. The pills come in packages of 24 and Malia has four packages. Will there be enough pills for two weeks? Will there be any left over?

4. Jonas takes three pills a day for three weeks for his infection. He starts at 1:00 p.m., Sept. 21. On what date does he finish?

Practice: Meaningful Remainders

Read and solve the problems. Think about what the remainder means in each situation. How will you deal with the remainder so that the answer makes sense?

1. Jody has $100 to spend on presents for her daughter's birthday. How many DVD's costing $22 each can she purchase?

2. A ferry can hold 30 cars. How many trips will it make to carry 175 cars across the river?

3. A 10-foot board of wood is to be cut into four pieces. How long will each piece be?

4. A rope is 75 feet long. How many nine-foot jump ropes can be made?

5. Sarah has $25 to spend on favors for her five-year-old son's birthday. How many matchbox trucks can she buy at $1.99 each?

6. Five people are planning a trip to New York City. They will share the expenses. The total cost of the trip will be $1,853. How much will each person have to pay?

7. A 12-foot sandwich is to be shared by eight people. How many feet of the sandwich will each person get?

8. Write a word problem for 29 ÷ 4. How will you deal with the remainder?

Mental Math Practice: Money in My Pocket

I have less than $100 in $1 bills in my pocket.

If I count my bills two at a time, I have one left over.

If I count them three at a time, I have none left over.

If I count them four, five, or six at a time, I always have three left over.

How many dollars are in my pocket?

Use this chart of numbers 1–100 to help you keep track as you think.

1	2	3	4	5	6	7	8	9	10
11	12	13	14	15	16	17	18	19	20
21	22	23	24	25	26	27	28	29	30
31	32	33	34	35	36	37	38	39	40
41	42	43	44	45	46	47	48	49	50
51	52	53	54	55	56	57	58	59	60
61	62	63	64	65	66	67	68	69	70
71	72	73	74	75	76	77	78	79	80
81	82	83	84	85	86	87	88	89	90
91	92	93	94	95	96	97	98	99	100

Test Practice

1. Caryn buys two bags of candy for Halloween. Each bag has 55 pieces of candy. She gives each child that comes to her door four pieces of candy. How many children will receive candy?

    (1) 13

    (2) 14

    (3) 26

    (4) 27

    (5) 30

2. Holiday paper cups come in packs of eight. Alberto expects no more than 15 people at his party. He needs three cups per person. If he buys enough packs, how many cups will he have left over?

    (1) None

    (2) 3

    (3) 5

    (4) 7

    (5) 8

3. Mei-Ling donated $1,600 for book prizes to three outstanding graduates. The money was divided evenly. How much money did each graduate receive?

    (1) $500

    (2) $525

    (3) $533.30

    (4) $533.33

    (5) $550

4. Boards come in 12-foot lengths. If Sal buys three boards and cuts each into 5′ lengths for shelves, how much wood will be left over as scrap?

    (1) 1′

    (2) 3′

    (3) 6′

    (4) 12′

    (5) None

5. A case of frozen pizzas costs $50. There are 12 pizzas in a case. Cases can be split to purchase individual pizzas. You need 28 pizzas for your party this week. How much will they cost?

    (1) About $100

    (2) About $115

    (3) About $125

    (4) About $150

    (5) About $200

6. Four co-workers share the 30 cookies they brought to the office. How many does each person get if the cookies are shared equally?

Closing the Unit: Computer Lab

> *How would you plan for your community?*

In this final assessment session, you will make a plan for how to spend up to $10,000 on equipment for a community center computer lab and make a presentation of your plan.

What will $10,000 buy? How much does computer equipment cost? What does the lab really need and what would be nice to have, but not essential? You will use what you have learned in earlier lessons to help you estimate, multiply, and add the numbers and make sure that your calculator results make sense.

Have fun spending money and demonstrating your mental math skills!

Activity 1: Computer Lab Project

You are on a committee planning a new computer lab for the community center. You estimate that the number of children and adults using the lab will be more than 250 each year, but for purposes of planning, you will figure on about 20 people using it each week.

Your committee received a $10,000 grant to buy equipment for the lab. You need to plan what to buy, bearing in mind that for this first year, the $10,000 grant is the only money you will have for equipment and supplies.

Use the catalog price list your teachers will give you. You may buy as many computers as you wish. However, for each computer you will need a keyboard, a mouse, and a power surge protector.

You will also need software to run programs on the computer, CD's and DVD's on which to save files, a printer, paper for copies, and ink cartridges for the printer.

Make a draft plan on page 179. You may use a calculator, *but you must estimate first* and record your estimates to get a sense of whether your answers are about right.

Use page 180 for your final plan.

Before you start the planning project, complete the four *Computer Lab Warm-Ups* on pages 174–78.

Computer Lab Warm-Up 1
Mental Math Calculations for Paper Use

When planning how much paper to purchase for a computer lab for a year, it is important to make good estimates of how much paper people will use.

Explain how you solved each of the following problems.

1. Assume 20 people will use the computer lab on a regular basis. How much paper will the lab need if each person uses

   a. 10 pages/year?

   b. 55 pages/year?

   c. 100 pages/year?

d. 120 pages/year?

e. 200 pages/year?

2. Assume 50 people will use the computer lab on a regular basis. How much paper will the lab need if each person uses

a. 20 pages/year?

b. 125 pages/year?

Computer Lab Warm-Up 2
How Much More for...?

1. a. How much more money will a laptop computer with a 17″ screen and a CD/DVD burner cost than a laptop with a 15.4″ screen? (Refer to the E-Z Computer Mail Order Catalog.)

b. Show and explain two ways you might find the answer. Use the number line to demonstrate one of the ways.

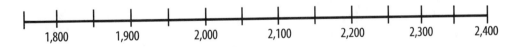

1,800   1,900   2,000   2,100   2,200   2,300   2,400

2. **a.** What is the cost difference between the least and the most expensive computers in the E-Z Computer Mail Order Catalog?

  b. Show and explain two ways you might find the answer.

Computer Lab Warm-Up 3
Inventory Count

Most offices take a regular inventory of supplies, especially when they plan to order more. They might also try to figure out how to store items so they can be counted quickly when an inventory is done.

1. If you bought 24 packs of CD's, sold 25 to a pack, there are many ways you could stack and store them. Show at least three ways you can think of to stack and store the 24 packs of CD's. Write an equation for each way you show.

2. If you looked in your office closet and saw each of the following arrangements, how many DVD's would you have on hand? Write an equation for each total.

Remember, there are 10 DVD's to a pack.

Each ☐ represents one pack.

a.

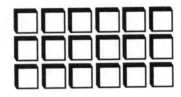

Equation: _____

b.

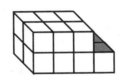

Equation: _____

c.

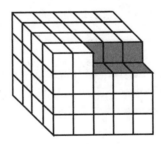

Equation: _____

Computer Lab Warm-Up 4
Item Costs

1. One way to approach setting up the computer lab is to decide how much you want to spend per workstation and figure out how many workstations you can provide based on that cost. Let's say you plan on spending about $1,500 per workstation.

   a. How many workstations can you provide with the $10,000 grant? Show all your work.

   b. Is there money left over? What would you do with that extra money?

2. Another way that you could approach setting up a lab is to consider how much space is available. Once you know how many workstations you could fit in your room, you can figure out how much money you have to spend per workstation.

   a. If you knew that you could fit only three workstations in the available space, about how much money could you spend on each?

   b. What is one way you could spend that amount (answer for 2a) to build a workstation? What would you buy?

Draft Plan for Computer Lab

Use this space to keep track of your estimates.

Items	Estimated Cost

Estimated grand total: _____

Final Plan for Computer Lab

Item Description	Quantity	Cost per Item	Total Cost

Actual grand total: _____

Activity 2: Final Assessment

First, you will do a mental math challenge. Then your teacher will show you some other problems and ask you to check off how you feel about your ability to solve them. In each case, check off one of the following:

___ Can do   ____ Don't know how   ____ Not sure

VOCABULARY

Lesson	Terms, Symbols, Concepts	Definitions and Examples
Opening the Unit	estimate	
	mental math	
1	approximate	
	rounding	
	sum	
2	10's place	
	100's place	
3	number line	
4	equation	
5	difference	
	negative numbers	
	positive numbers	

VOCABULARY *(continued)*

Lesson	Terms, Symbols, Concepts	Definitions and Examples
5	range	
7	order of operations	
	parentheses	
8	equivalent expressions	
	exponent	
	square number	
11	factors	
12	remainder	

REFLECTIONS

OPENING THE UNIT: Everyday Numbers

What did you find out about your strong points? What challenged you?

_____

_____

_____

_____

_____

_____

_____

LESSON 1: Close Enough with Mental Math

Describe your favorite way of estimating a total for a number of items.

_____

_____

_____

_____

_____

_____

_____

_____

What is most challenging for you when you try to estimate a total in your head?

_____

_____

_____

_____

_____

_____

_____

_____

LESSON 2: Mental Math in the Checkout Line

Give an example of when it would be good to "round and adjust" with mental math in your everyday life.

_____

_____

_____

_____

_____

_____

_____

_____

LESSON 3: Traveling with Numbers

List three things you want to remember about making and using a number line.

_____

_____

_____

_____

_____

_____

_____

_____

LESSON 4: Traveling in Time

Describe two different ways to mentally calculate the age of someone born in 1965.

_____

_____

_____

_____

_____

_____

_____

_____

How are addition and subtraction related?

_____

_____

_____

_____

_____

_____

_____

LESSON 5: Extending the Line

What do you know about negative numbers?

_____

_____

_____

_____

_____

_____

_____

_____

What do you know about finding the difference between any two numbers?

_____

_____

_____

_____

_____

_____

_____

_____

LESSON 6: Take Your Winnings

What would you like to remember about the make-up of whole numbers?

_____

_____

_____

_____

_____

_____

_____

What short-cuts did you use that you found helpful?

_____

_____

_____

_____

_____

_____

_____

_____

_____

LESSON 7: Patterns and Order

What did you learn when using a calculator?

_____

_____

_____

_____

_____

_____

_____

_____

_____

What did you learn about order of operations?

_____

_____

_____

_____

_____

_____

_____

LESSON 8: Picture This

Show an example of a picture, an equation, and a story that connect to one another.

_____

_____

_____

_____

_____

_____

_____

LESSON 9: What's the Story?

What did you learn today about ways to solve problems?

_____

_____

_____

_____

_____

_____

_____

_____

LESSON 10: Deal Me In

Explain how division and multiplication are related.

_____

_____

_____

_____

_____

_____

_____

_____

Grade yourself on your ability to use mental math to solve division problems. Do you need to improve?

_____

_____

_____

_____

_____

_____

_____

_____

LESSON 11: String It Along

Write a word problem and draw a picture for each of the following:

Split 60 into five parts

_____

_____

_____

_____

_____

_____

_____

_____

Find how many 5's are in 60.

●

_____

_____

_____

_____

_____

_____

_____

LESSON 12: Making Do

What did you learn today about remainders?

_____

_____

_____

_____

●

_____

_____

_____

How can you write remainders using fractions? Decimals? Whole numbers and "r"?

_____

_____

_____

_____

_____

_____

_____

_____

●

CLOSING THE UNIT: Computer Lab

What are the most important ideas and skills you have learned in this unit?

_____

_____

_____

_____

_____

_____

_____

What are you best at?

_____

_____

_____

_____

_____

_____

_____

Where would you like to improve?

_____

_____

_____

_____

_____

_____

_____